AT A
GIVEN MOMENT

FAITH MATTERS IN HEALTHCARE

AT A
GIVEN MOMENT

FAITH MATTERS IN HEALTHCARE

GRAHAM MCALL

Published by Christian Medical Fellowship
6 Marshalsea Road, London SE1 1HL, UK
www.cmf.org.uk

ISBN 978-0-906747-41-4

Printed by Yeomans – www.yeomansmarketing.co.uk
Cover design by S2 Design & Advertising – enquiries@s2design.co.uk

CONTENTS

PREFACE

T his book is a collection of anecdotes and personal reflections on issues of worldview and faith in healthcare encounters. In the UK, by 2009 any sharing of faith in medical consultations was controversial. I write as a Christian [1] to contribute to this debate and my first thesis is that medicine that is centred on the patient should often include a spiritual history, if that is appropriate to the patient. This is so, irrespective of the clinician's worldview.

I hope you will enjoy the stories and find encouragement and challenge. Please bear with me and maybe by the end you will agree that there is a missing dimension in the way that many of us work. Though I write primarily for clinicians, I think parts of this book will be of relevance or interest to many.

Stories from a variety of healthcare contexts make up the core of the text. I am grateful for the many patients, support staff and healthcare workers from different parts of the world who have spent time telling me their experiences. I have changed the details of patients and clinicians, while endeavouring not to compromise the integrity of each example. Others have kindly allowed me to quote previously published stories. I sought tales that might encourage or educate in this area, and have tried to include the negative along with the positive. I always learnt far more from my mistakes than my successes, and some of my mistakes have been spectacularly stupid![2] Thank you especially to those of you who have shared your failures.

Some of the stories are stated without much comment and I want to state clearly here that I don't approve of everything that was said and done. You will have to decide what you think yourself (and how you would have done things better!) For me it has been a fascinating privilege to hear these 'dispatches from the Front' and I have been excited by the variety of ways people respond to these issues.

It is not a good idea to suggest something new to busy professionals! In our target driven lives taking on something new usually means some other good activity has to stop. I'm writing with the conviction that an understanding of worldview will save time, both for the healthcare worker and the patient.

Why *At a Given Moment*? There comes a moment, often brief, in many conversations with patients when if we are really listening with an open mind a new insight into their underlying problem comes to light.[3] Then a fundamental shift in the patient's understanding (and even worldview) may occur if it is well handled. This 'Eureka'[4] moment is given by the patient; they have opened a window and invited you to join them in considering their situation. I believe the moment has also been given by a loving God. The question is – what do we do with it?

I hope you will come away from this book excited, but also with many questions. Some of the topics are enormous in themselves and my selection of ideas and examples is necessarily eclectic. The references will point you in some useful directions.

ACKNOWLEDGEMENTS

I am unsure how grateful I should be to Andrew Sharp or to my son Lewis who both pushed me to write! Certainly it has been my dear wife Jenny who has required measureless patience, and without her encouragement you would be doing something else just now!

Thanks also to Andrew Fergusson and Kevin Vaughan and the team at Christian Medical Fellowship UK, to Dianne Vescovi and Bob Snyder of *International Saline*, and to Martin and Elizabeth Goldsmith for all their support and invaluable advice.

Lastly to my many friends (teachers, colleagues, students and patients) I send greetings – may you experience the given moment to the full.

At a Given Moment

1. INTRODUCTION

O ur purpose as healthcare workers is to replace the evil of illness with the goodness of health. We treasure human life. [5] Our first task is the prevention of disease, and when prevention fails we work for cure, and when cure is not possible we aim to sustain and comfort until the death of the body. Raised from the dust of the earth, illness and death are inescapable parts of our brief existence. When they occur in our lives or the lives of those close to us, these events not only have an enormous impact on us physically, but also psychologically, socially and spiritually. Our reaction to illness and death, both personally and communally, is determined by our view of the nature of reality.

In the past two centuries western medicine has taken a reductionist [6] approach to the development of new treatments with great success. In so many areas we take for granted now the wonders of what has been achieved already – anaesthesia, immunisation, antibiotics, fertility control, joint replacement, antipsychotic drugs – to name just a few. It is right to celebrate this wonderful work. With these tools at our disposal, medical professionals can become quite comfortable within the healthcare machine, and become familiar with dealing with illness day by day in our rather detached 'disease palaces'. [7]

But to the uninitiated patient the success in extending life expectancy has been so marked that, when disease and death do strike, it is often (and perhaps more so than in previous generations) an existential shock. This shock can be intensified because of rising consumer expectations. [8] Advertising bombards us with images of perfect bodies achievable with some product or system. The patient comes to view his body as just another item that can be fixed, much like a broken car. Then he is taken by surprise at the impact of illness on life, and the time it all takes. As a result, there is some disappointment with medicine. If there is much we can do, there is so much that we cannot. Good medical care may give transient worthwhile relief from disease, but one of the things it can't deliver is contentment.

As the realisation of an illness grows, patients place themselves in the care of health teams. Where and when a patient consults, and how they accept and respond to treatment, are governed by many factors beyond a reductionist approach. We clinicians get frustrated when patient behaviours can wreck well planned treatments! I remember the caustic comments that my senior wrote in a patient's notes: 'This betzopenic twit...' [9], after a young man who had had a perfectly good plaster cast applied the previous day for a serious leg fracture then wrecked it in an alcoholic binge. He was supposed not to bear weight through the broken leg, and had not only done so in unsanitary conditions, but had also had a good hack at the plaster as well for good measure.

It is folly to ignore the whole person while trying to treat the illness. In the case of the young man, perhaps it may have been prudent to recognise at the start that he would not give grateful attention or exemplary care to looking after his leg plaster! We now know well (or should do) the importance of assessing physical problems in the psychological and social context before reaching a verdict on the best treatment to advise. But in addition, there is something else that we are often missing: it is the patient's and clinician's worldview. There is the possibility that we can connect at a deeper level, to the benefit of both. Behaviour is determined by values; values are determined by beliefs. Everyone has beliefs.

However, raising worldview, faith and spiritual issues with patients isn't always easy. And when we recognise that the clinician is not some diagnostic therapeutic machine but another human with a different worldview, things can begin to get untidy. In the UK a nurse was suspended for offering to pray with a patient, [10] a hostel worker has been sacked for discussing moral views with a colleague on night duty [11] and the financing of chaplaincy in government hospitals was attacked. [12] Even a council worker in a housing interview was sacked, against the client's wishes, for suggesting hope in God in informal discussion. [13]

Clinicians (and hospital chaplains!) have become uneasy. Is the mention of faith in consultations really an unprofessional breach of contractual obligation, an intrusion into privacy, and an imposition on the vulnerable? Is it going to propel the clinician into a disciplinary proceeding? Or is there another view – that it should be a regular or even obligatory part of medical history taking and therapy planning?

Any personal encounter with another human being involves some element of risk taking. As a medical encounter proceeds, the patient will be making running decisions about how much to trust the doctor or nurse, so that perhaps after a relatively trivial issue is dealt with, the patient then makes up their mind to trust you (or not as the case may be) and, if so, says 'I've never told anyone this before, but ...' and out comes the often tragic tale that has blighted their life ever since some traumatic event.

The patient has taken the risk of trusting you; the burden they were carrying needs to be unloaded. But at the same time you are trusting them. Your reputation and career are in the hands of your patients. While you are obliged to respect their confidence, they are not obliged to respect yours – after all, this time together belongs, in a very real sense, to the patient. Exploring worldview involves some risk taking in the same way that any history taking or therapeutic help involves some risk. But it is no excuse for reckless impulsiveness. Like prescribing an antibiotic, side effects sometimes occur! In clinical encounters we are humans together, trying to unravel the mysteries of illness and life.

I stand in awe at the courage of some patients and colleagues. Sometimes there is a boldness which places political correctness on one side to confront worldview issues in the consulting room. These issues may be relatively simple, as when a patient asks me to lie on a medical certificate; or complex, as for example when dealing with therapy at the end of life.

Fear of discussing beliefs needs to go. Exploring the worldview dimension of a consultation isn't something magical or different from other aspects, even if at first it feels unfamiliar. It is a matter of acquiring some knowledge, learning some skills, and being willing to change some of our attitudes. Such a process is a normal activity for anyone making a personal professional development plan. Generally, those who are fearful need to learn boldness, and the bold need to learn gentleness and sensitivity, while keeping in mind that the patient may have chosen you because they are comfortable with your approach as it is!

Even if there are few neat and tidy answers in the messiness and complexity of medical encounters, exploration of worldview (sometimes very brief) can suggest solutions and changes which would not otherwise have appeared. To me it often seems to have been the smallest of gestures of shared humanity or expressed faith that have had the most remarkable impact, so don't despise the small things.

Is it really possible, through our work, to help 'make the wounded whole'? [14] I hope so. This hope is founded on my belief that we are not alone in clinical encounters – the loving Creator is right there, sustaining and waiting, and giving us this particular time, this 'space of grace'. [15]

2. THE IMPORTANCE OF PATIENTS' WORLDVIEWS

A GP'S STORY

'I know the score, Doc.' Fred, a 68 year old lifelong smoker, had been diagnosed with incurable lung cancer. I had been Fred's GP for a few years and from other family members I knew he'd been a very difficult man to live with, but a friend, Carol, had given him a home as he was dying when no one else would. She sat with him now as we discussed their questions and I tried to explore their concerns and sketch out something of the problems they might face together as the cancer progressed, and what support was available. Finally I asked, 'Fred, do you have a faith to support you at a time like this?'

'Oh, I don't have any time for that stuff' he replied, but then Carol said, 'When his wife was alive she went to church, and I've arranged for the minister to come round tomorrow'. I thought to myself that the minister could be in for a short visit.

'May I say something personal?' I asked. 'Go ahead,' said Fred. 'If it wasn't for Jesus, I wouldn't be here looking after you.' Fred didn't ask me how or why that might be true, but said how much he appreciated the medical care.

Thinking back on my time with Fred, I realised I was actually irritated with him. I had spent much time trying to deal with the consequences of his poor parenting skills. His was a very dysfunctional family and I had spent hours trying to help his sons who were frequently intoxicated. Fred was generally oblivious to the mayhem he had caused in the past, and seemed to assume he had the right for all his needs to be met by others. He had little idea of the immense cost to the community of all this, or the investment in resources to support them.

But behind this lay an even greater reality: thousands of years of investment by a loving God. Fred was unaware of how God had dealt with me in my life, or my background. During my upbringing my parents and grandparents had told their tales of how God had saved them at impossible moments. And Fred was unaware that if Jesus hadn't intervened in my own life in many ways, doubtless diverting me from all sorts of disasters, I wouldn't have been anywhere near this sort of clinic. By saying, 'If it wasn't for Jesus...' I was trying to give him a quick insight into where I was coming from, and to challenge his dismissive attitude.

Over the course of the next few weeks of home visits until Fred's death we didn't speak of it again (and I never heard how the minister got on!) I'd like to go back and run the original consultation again, but I can't. If I'd been listening a bit more carefully, maybe I would have responded to his statement with another question. The truth is that I never discovered why he had 'no time for that stuff'. And I can't now recall how I responded to his thanks; probably with a slightly insincere 'You're welcome'. Also, I had asked about his beliefs as a last question, as if it was a question you'd only ask in the direst of circumstances, as a sort of parting shot – if all else fails, turn to God. How come, as his physician, I didn't already have a grasp of what he felt gave meaning to his life?

I had only very cursorily tried to establish Fred's beliefs as he faced death. I had then tried a one shot statement, almost as a desperate attempt to make him think again. I wanted him to be aware of the fact that without Jesus, whole swathes of the caring structures in his life would be absent. And, yes, I wanted him to know, despite my impatience, that he was immensely loved, far more that he could imagine, by a God who wanted him to enjoy life for ever and who longed for a 'yes' to that invitation.

As a Christian I can't abandon who I am at the consulting room door. In fact, it is being a Christian that got me in there in the first place. But I never heard what Fred's beliefs were. I had failed to take a coherent history. Despite all this, he trusted me, and he and his family accepted my fumbling as a genuine expression of care. Maybe, I don't know, what I said was what he needed to hear. Not a smooth professional performance, but a heart's cry from one human to another.

Whether they are aware of it or not, everyone has a worldview, a view of the world and their place in it. This story reveals something of the doctor's worldview and some glimpses of the patient's. The expression 'worldview'[16] is a translation of the German word *Weltanschauung*, which describes a comprehensive view of human life and the world, a set of beliefs held by an individual or by a group.

Our worldview determines our attitudes, values and behaviours. Possessing a worldview need not imply a closed mind, or that its possessor assumes it answers all the questions of life. It is more a working hypothesis of what his life is all about, and it enables immense shortcuts in decision making. Worldviews are by no means confined to people with religious beliefs.

The consequences of having a worldview are all around us. A patient walks into a consulting room and sits down on a chair. They trust that the chair won't collapse. They understand that the clinic will have sourced chairs from a reasonable manufacturer, and don't want their patients to fall to the floor. There are years of experience and cultural understanding that enable this sensible shortcut. The patient doesn't have to give it a moment's thought. That is faith in action. The faith is placed in the clinic, the health service, the chair manufacturers and the consistency of the laws of nature (in this case gravity). Life without faith would be utterly impractical. A worldview gives a practical 'rule of thumb' for day to day living. Faith is the activity of putting a worldview or belief into trusting action. [17]

MAKING ASSUMPTIONS ABOUT
A PATIENT'S WORLDVIEW

Often the worldview of a group or individual includes unspoken assumptions about life that have never been questioned. So, for example, in the UK we assume 'first come, first served' and queuing in line is fair – woe betide an international visitor or 'rude' Briton who goes directly to the front! This is just a shared understanding of justice, fairness and a communal behaviour: it is the 'way things are' and 'everyone knows that, it's obvious'. Not being willing to queue is socially unacceptable and stigmatised. But the practice actually flows from a worldview regarding the fundamental equality of value of individual people, which has deep roots in our cultural and religious heritage.

Assumptions like these can make cross-cultural interactions especially hazardous. Other societies may be more willing to sacrifice the individual for the good of the community as a whole. So, to take one recent example, the decision to execute a man with severe mental illness who was convicted of drug smuggling may seem entirely wrong to one community and yet entirely right to another. [18]

Glance at the worldview chart (pp10-11) that classifies and compares worldviews, and consider what might be different in the way an adherent of each major group might see illness in themselves and others.

Even in a multicultural society it is easy for a well-educated clinician to make assumptions about a patient's worldview, so we need to proceed with caution.

A PATIENT'S STORY [19]

We visited our GP and told him that we thought my wife was about six weeks pregnant. It had been seven years since our last child had been born. The GP immediately said, 'Would you like me to arrange an abortion?' to which I replied, tongue in cheek, 'No thanks, we'd thought we'd kill one of our existing children and keep this one'.

A NURSE'S STORY[20]

I was on duty in the Casualty department and a mother came in with two children, one of whom was ill. The child who was not ill had to wait while the others went in, and objected. Mother reassured him that his guardian angel would look after him. So he sat, waiting. He was sitting quietly, alone, doing nothing except swinging his legs a bit and looking content. After some time I went over and sat down beside him.

His mother eventually emerged and said: 'See, your guardian angel did look after you'. Immediately the little boy burst into floods of tears. 'Oh dear!' mother said, 'What's the matter?' 'That lady!' And he pointed an accusing finger at me, 'She sat on my guardian angel!'

It is not a good idea to sit on someone's guardian angel.

A GP'S STORY

A 34 year old Asian lady attended with recurrent urinary infections. She was also suffering from infertility, and there had been several mistakes and misunderstandings in ensuring that all the lab investigations required for the infertility referral had been done correctly. I apologised for the errors and made arrangements to ensure everything was done. As far as the urinary infections were concerned, she had already been fully investigated and all obvious causes excluded.

'So why do the infections keep happening, then?' she asked. 'Well you're just unlucky, but it's good we haven't found any serious cause, and we'll treat each one as it happens.' She seemed a little annoyed and persisted, 'Yes, but if all the tests are normal and they keep coming there must be a reason'.

I replied: 'If there is a reason I'm afraid we can't identify it, so it's just bad luck and we'll treat each episode as it comes – obviously if you have any other ideas or we think of anything else useful to check along the way, we can do that'.

She looked even more unhappy. Later I heard that she had complained about my attitude to a colleague; she said I had accused

	REALITY	MAN
NATURALISM Atheism; Agnosticism; Existentialism	The material universe is all that exists. Reality is "one-dimensional." There is no such thing as a soul or a spirit. Everything can be explained on the basis of natural law.	Man is the chance product of a biological process of evolution. Man is entirely material. The human species will one day pass out of existence.
PANTHEISM Hinduism; Taoism; Buddhism; much New Age Consciousness	Only the spiritual dimension exists. All else is illusion, maya. Spiritual reality, Brahman, is eternal, impersonal, and unknowable. It is possible to say that everything is a part of God, or that God is in everything and everyone.	Man is one with ultimate reality. Thus man is spiritual, eternal, and impersonal. Man's belief that he is an individual is illusion.
THEISM Judaism; Christianity; Islam	An infinite, personal God exists. He created a finite, material world. Reality is both material and spiritual. The universe as we know it had a beginning and is moving towards a consummation.	Humankind is the unique creation of God. People were created "in the image of God," which means amongst other things that we are individual persons, creative and responsible physical and spiritual. We are potentially eternal.
SPIRITISM AND POLYTHEISM Thousands of Religions	The world is populated by spirit beings who govern what goes on. Gods and demons are the real reason behind "natural" events. Material things are real, but they have spirits associated with them and, therefore, can be interpreted spiritually.	Man is a creation of the gods like the rest of the creatures on earth. Often, tribes or races have a special relationship with some gods who protect them and can punish them.
POSTMODERNISM	Reality must be interpreted through our language and cultural "paradigm." Therefore, reality is "socially constructed."	Humans are nodes in a cultural reality – they are a product of their social setting.

TRUTH	VALUES
Truth is usually understood as scientific proof. Only that which can be observed with the five senses is accepted as real or true.	No objective values or morals exist. Morals are individual preferences or socially useful behaviors. Even social morals are subject to evolution and change.
Truth is an experience of unity with "the oneness" of the universe. Truth is beyond all rational description. Rational thought as it is understood in the West cannot show us reality.	Because ultimate reality is impersonal, many pantheistic thinkers believe that there is no real distinction between good and evil. Instead, "unenlightened" behavior is that which fails to understand essential unity.
Truth about God is known through revelation. Truth about the material world is gained via revelation and the five senses in conjunction with rational thought.	Moral values are the objective expression of an absolute moral being.
Truth about the natural world is discovered through the shaman figure who has visions telling him what the gods and demons are doing and how they feel.	Moral values take the form of taboos, which are things that irritate or anger various spirits. These taboos are different from the idea of "good and evil' because it is just as important to avoid irritating evil spirits as it is good ones.
Truths are mental constructs meaningful to individuals within a particular cultural paradigm. They do not apply to other paradigms. Truth is relative to one's culture.	Values are part of our social paradigms as well. Tolerance, freedom of expression, inclusion, and refusal to claim to have the answers are the only universal values.

This chart is modified from Xenos Christian Fellowship: *www.xenos.org/classes/papers/5wldview.htm* adapted from McCallum D. *Christianity: The Faith That Makes Sense.* Revised 1997. Tyndale.

her of being unlucky. A friend familiar with her worldview explained she would have thought that I was accusing her of having bad karma and that I was implying she should just accept it – and that her infertility, the mix-up with her results, and her recurrent infections were all evidence of bad karma and there was really no point getting flustered about it. In a way it was all her fault. The fact that I'd accused her of being unlucky really negated any apology!

MAKING ASSUMPTIONS ABOUT A COLLEAGUE'S WORLDVIEW

On our local GP training scheme it is acknowledged that behaviour stems from attitudes, attitudes arise from values, and values arise from a worldview. When we work together in a hospital with colleagues of other worldviews we do it on the basis of a common set of behaviours that are acceptable. Indeed such is the variety of values that we hold that these behaviours have to be formalised into General Medical Council guidelines which make statements that to some are blindingly obvious.

Take honesty, for example. Is this not a universal principle which everyone understands as essential in healthcare? Not at all. When I taught in a medical school in south east Asia and invited friends from one cultural grouping to dinner, they would invariably reply 'yes', but then as often as not they would never arrive. When we made discreet enquiry we were informed it was very rude to decline an invitation, but quite polite not to arrive! We strongly warned medical students there who were going on electives in the UK that it was perfectly OK to decline an invitation, but that if they accepted they must attend. 'Really?' was the reaction, 'How strange!'

Similarly in the clinical situation, a lie was often more acceptable than offering patients access to uncomfortable truth. A friend who worked in central Asia explained that doctors often concealed the truth (for example about a hopeless prognosis or untreatable condition) for a number of reasons. First, it was so that patients would not feel bad – it would be unkind to tell the truth. Secondly, it could be a matter of personal honour; one would not want to admit one could not help. Thirdly, there were financial issues – admission for a course of useless treatment could supplement a clinician's meagre income. Then there was the possibility that in a totalitarian state it was illegal, and in some religious systems even theologically unacceptable, to say that there was little treatment available.

Some of these reasons for lying to patients should make some of us in the UK uncomfortable in our target-driven health service and private practices. Without a deeply held worldview reason to be honest the strictest codes will be weak.

SUFFERING AND DIFFERENT WORLDVIEWS

Questions about the origins and meaning of suffering are dealt with in different ways by the different worldviews. In fact it could be said that religions are often judged by their response to the problem of suffering. All doctors need to have at least some grasp of how people view their suffering,[21] and to have great humility as they tread in this area. One obvious example is that if someone believes that their suffering is a punishment from almighty God, they may feel they should just accept it and do nothing about it. They may even obstruct your attempts to help, seeing in them a disrespect for, or interference with, the divine will.

Here are some clues, stated very briefly. Hindus believe in karma, an exact balancing of good and evil which occurs partly through reincarnation. The suffering of a patient is because of misdeeds in this life or a former life, and must just be accepted. The Buddha taught that all suffering is in the mind and thus illusory, and taught the art of detachment through meditation.

The monotheistic religions teach the sovereignty of almighty God over all events. This then presents the problem: if God is good, why does he allow evil and suffering? Some will be fearful of even asking the question 'Why?' if they are taught that it is sinful to doubt.

A GP'S STORY

At the age of 24, Ali had been out on an errand in his home city in Somalia when a bomb hit the house in which his family were living. Most of his family were killed. On one occasion as we were talking I said, 'You're a Muslim, aren't you?' 'Yes,' he said. 'So tell me, from your position, where is God in all of this?'

He said, 'You know, John, if I understood why all this happened, then I would be God'. I said, 'Your faith is remarkable, and it reminds me of Abraham'. I pulled down a Bible and showed him where it is written: 'Abraham believed the Lord, and he credited it to him as righteousness'. [22]

While we can see some uses of pain [23] and understand the principle of 'No pain, no gain' [24] in sport (or cosmetic surgery!), monotheists are left with the problem of apparently pointless suffering. The Muslim answer is summed up in the word *Islam*, which means 'to submit'. It involves accepting the present limits to our intelligence and understanding, for the hope of paradise after death. The Jewish answer is that suffering has a purpose which we don't yet comprehend but which also looks to eternal life. The Christian answer [25] is that God became a man in Jesus Christ and entered suffering himself. He did this so that men might be rescued from their evil for a bodily resurrection when heaven comes to transform earth in a future that is free of suffering. [26] In this view present suffering is allowed temporarily for a greater good.

Atheism asserts that we need to face the fact that we are alone: there is no spiritual realm to be considered, and man is just subject to the physical laws of the universe of which suffering is a natural part. In this last view suffering only has any temporary significance that we choose to give it (in so far as choice has any reality).

Clearly, no religion has a fully satisfying answer to the 'Why?' question in the here and now. Perhaps the more productive question when faced with suffering is 'What for?'

It only requires a moment's thought about this extremely simplified summary to realise that patients who are facing illness and death will have very different views as to how they would like to manage things.

A GP'S STORY[27]

I once met a woman who had been badly crippled in an accident caused by a drunken driver. To begin with as she lay in hospital, she was angry and resentful. She found herself again and again asking 'Why?' One day, instead of 'Why?' she began to ask herself 'What for?'

Immediately she began to think of all she had learned from the experience, and how her whole life would have a different value because of it. She took an interest in the patient in the next bed and found she could help her with her difficulties. When she left hospital, she found she could no longer dash around being busy; she had more time for people who visited her. By the time I met her, although she could only walk with the help of two sticks and was constantly in pain, she had an infectious gaiety which anyone might envy.

Disease and pain challenge a person's worldview acutely. It causes them to re-examine the meaning of their life. They also become 'a patient'.

THE INTERNAL NARRATIVE

Then into this situation comes a multicultural team; the ambulance crew, the nurses, the porters, the physicians, the cleaners, all with their own worldviews. Each will have their own perspective on illness. Some of the team may be Christians who bring a unique perspective on suffering derived from their faith. Christians see our individual and communal life stories fitting into God's big story ('metanarrative'[28]) and this gives a sense of being part of the great sweep of history, part of something bigger, much bigger in fact – God himself. This is foundational for us; it gives us a sense of unique time and place.

Paul, the apostle, puts this clearly: '[God] determined the times set for men and the exact places where they should live. God did this so that men would seek him and perhaps reach out for him and find him, though he is not far from each one of us.'[29] As Christians we believe that we have been brought to this exact place and encounter in the plan of God at this unique moment in history, with the opportunity to find him and to do good.

This is as true of the consultation with its intense concentration and multi-level communication, as it is true of other moments of life. Of course we regularly get it wrong, but there is the grace of forgiveness through Christ [30] (and often from the patients!) when we do, and we try to move on. And it's messy; frequently we have little idea why the suffering we witness is permitted, but we believe it is important. We hang on because at the heart of Christianity is the message of a God who entered our suffering and overcame it. [31]

If we have this worldview and know how foundational it is for us, then we can appreciate how important it is for our patients. During illness, the small issues of daily life become less important and the questions come to the fore: Why me? Why now?

We won't know what is going on in the core of the patient's thinking if we don't ask. Physicians should ask about how their patients view life. This needs to be done at the right time, with the patient's needs central. Sensitivity, permission and respect are paramount. It should not be voyeuristic – an exploration only for our satisfaction because it is an area of personal interest to us. A patient's worldview not only affects their view of the past and present but also their view of the future too – their view of the future has an immensely powerful impact on the way they react to the present. Sometimes a clinician should bring this into focus for the patient.

A GP's STORY

Sometimes when I've seen a patient with some psychological or relationship difficulty, or perhaps when a mild depression is resolving, it strikes me that one reason for their confusion is that they haven't consciously worked out what they think their life is about.

So I say something like, 'Correct me if I'm wrong but I get the impression that you haven't really decided why you are on this planet. Is there something that you feel passionate about? If it was ten years from now and you looked back, what accomplishment would really satisfy you? Why don't you take this opportunity and take time to look at the big questions, or you'll find life has passed you by before you get round to it.'

A PATIENT'S STORY

When I was growing up, I always felt I had to do just a little bit more to get my parents' approval. Somehow I could never get it right. I had this fear that I might be abandoned. They were practical, pragmatic parents who were not given to physical affection towards me. My father felt that as long as he had provided for our physical needs he had done his duty. So I wasn't reassured. And in church I felt I was never quite good enough and I felt I was being pushed into a mould which wasn't me. So I drifted away. I withdrew from relationships. At least if I was independent I wouldn't be abandoned.

But my mental health suffered and I struggled to keep my head above water with work. I sought the help of doctors and over 30 years several well-meaning physicians tried to help me. They put in a lot of effort, but looking back I wish that one of them had been prepared to raise issues of faith at some stage and to recognise that it was pertinent in my case. I didn't expect them to be experts but they were ignoring a big part of me and the part which, in the end, contained the solution. It wasn't a chemical problem, it was a psychological and spiritual problem.

Then I encountered a Christian speaker who thought 'outside the box' and to whom there was no issue that was taboo. His refreshing honesty and fearlessness helped me grasp that love is not conditional and that God will never abandon you. You don't have to reach his standard or be perfect before he is for you. There is nothing that will be a revelation to him about me because he knows me fully. I had permission to be me.

'I don't fit into a box', I said to the speaker. He said 'And neither should you, sister'. This understanding of the depth of God's love was the key to change. And now I think I realise where part of my problems came from. I remember the moment when, at the age of 18 months, my mother left me standing screaming in a cot in a hospital ward. I remember the feeling of utter desolation, a desolation which my parents, for an assortment of reasons, were unable to touch over the years and which infected my view of God.

> *At the core of my mental illness was the sense that God had abandoned me and when I finally understood the depth of his willingness to sacrifice for me, disabling fear fell away.*
>
> *I don't know at what point I could have really grasped this, but maybe if a doctor had had the confidence to enquire about how I saw God I could have moved forwards sooner.*

If we don't ask about worldview, important clues or approaches will be missed. Useful comfort will be lost, therapeutic options and arguments in their favour will be omitted. Coping strategies and supports might not be identified. Monroe and colleagues [32] found that while 85% of American physicians felt that a spiritual history was important, less than 10% actually enquired about it.

Christians are far from alone in seeing their lives as a coherent story. Jeremy Holmes coined the phrase 'Autobiographical competence' [33] to describe the process by which we create a narrative and understand our lives. This complex internal personal story is reformed and constantly adjusted as we accept new ideas about ourselves, others and the world. Life crises, illness included, can create a crisis of autobiography. Fear and helplessness may disable our ability to add a coherent layer to our life story. And as Gwen Adshead [34,35,36] explains it, severe traumas of guilt after committed evil, or depersonalisation after suffered evil, can render a patient incoherent and unable to narrate their own story, even to themselves. These issues create a severely unresolved worldview.

A GP'S STORY

I have a 43 year old male patient with severe anxiety. He is an imaginative perfectionist with obsessive traits. He has suffered past trauma. He shakes with unfocused fear as he sits in the consulting room. He tells me hasn't slept all night before coming because he has been trying to work out the best way to explain his symptoms as he is so worried he'll get it wrong.

After the consultation he won't sleep because he'll working over in his mind exactly what was said by him, and was it right, and what was said and done by me, and what were the hidden meanings.

> *He can't make sense of what is happening, he will not rest even when*
> *he has gone over everything, in case he has missed something. Not*
> *surprisingly he is a virtual prisoner in his flat and misuses alcohol.*

This man's anxiety means he has a continual crisis of 'autobiographical competence'. He is unable to make the shortcuts that a coherent worldview would facilitate. It is not just major trauma or mental illness that can challenge someone's worldview. I'm struck how even minor illness can do that. I remember several discussions with adult patients attending after having had a sore throat for one day. 'You have a viral sore throat', I explain. 'But it hurts!' they respond. 'Yes', I have said (sometimes, I regret, with a touch of impatience), 'I'm sorry, sore throats can be terribly painful, that is why they are called "sore"'.

And I reflect to myself how soft we have become, how disconnected, cosseted and unimaginative, that even a sore throat comes as a considerable shock. Not surprising then how we are rocked by the betrayal of adultery, bereavement, torture, redundancy, sudden homelessness, or a major diagnosis. That degree of trauma will necessarily test our preconceived ideas to their roots.

WHEN WORLDVIEW IS CHALLENGED

There is good evidence for this in the changes in worldview of internees after the trauma of the prison camps in the Second World War; sometimes bringing religious belief where there was none, sometimes destroying it. Indeed the experience of trauma on the massive scale of the World Wars changed worldviews across whole systems of belief.

In these situations the 'Why?' question can become especially acute for the individual. Normal life stops. There may be acute emotional or physical pain. In his succinct and penetrating book on suffering, John Dickson [37] describes how as a nine year old he reacted to the death of his father. He was from a family that was not at all religious. Yet a few days after his dad died in an air crash he approached his mother with the question: 'Why did God let Dad's plane crash?' And later in the same book he goes on to describe how a friend of his, a convinced atheist, when faced with immense sorrow, found himself unable to resist the impulse to cry out 'Why?' in his head.

And when we come face to face with our own mortality, our worldview is tested through and through. The temptation for doctors is to shy away from patients once the possibility of cure is past, generally being uncomfortable with the idea that all treatment merely delays ultimate bodily failure. It is not only patients who, like Woody Allen[38], would prefer not to be there at the moment of their death. A lot of doctors would like to avoid being around at their patient's demise too!

What is it that bothers dying people the most? Common requests for physician assisted suicide in Oregon[39] are found to be centred on fear or loss. Patients feared losing autonomy (91%), enjoyment of life (87%), dignity (85%) and control of bodily functions (56%). They also feared pain (22%) and being a burden to others (37%).

Good history taking about a patient's worldview offers the clinician a window into this existential distress, and the possibility of helping the patient to find significant comfort and ability to address these specific issues. But there is another good reason why a clinician needs to clarify a patient's worldview: religious faith has an impact on health, and not just after resurrection! Before learning how to take a good history, it is worth examining something of what we know of the health effects of different worldviews.

3. THE IMPACT OF FAITH ON HEALTH OUTCOMES

A GP'S STORY

I was seeing a middle aged businessman. As he stood up to leave at the end of a consultation about low mood I said: 'So life has been very tough recently. Before you go can I just ask – have you ever been tempted to end it all?'

'Yes' he said, and sank back into the chair. 'Would you like to tell me about it?' I asked. 'It's not very nice.' 'Go ahead; it's OK to tell me.'

'It has to do with railway bridges' he said. 'And have you been on any bridges recently?' 'Yesterday.' 'What stopped you?' I asked. 'Well, I'm a Catholic...' and he tailed off into silence. 'And you thought God wouldn't be very happy to see you just yet?' We both laughed, and then came the tears...

This man's worldview saved him from committing suicide when he was depressed. In many ways worldview can have an immense impact on how patients respond to disease in themselves and in others. Harold Koenig of Duke University found substantial evidence that the practice of a religious faith affected clinical outcomes: [40]

'First, religious practice is one of the most common ways that patients cope with medical illness, and it predicts both successful coping and faster remission from depression in medical settings. Second, religious beliefs have been found to influence medical decisions that patients with serious medical illness make. Third, the faith community is a primary source of support for many medically ill patients, and social support has been associated with better adherence to therapy and medical outcomes. Fourth, based on a survey of 1,732,562 patients representing 33% of all hospitals in the United States, patient satisfaction with the emotional and spiritual aspects of care had one of the lowest ratings among all clinical care indicators and was one of the highest areas in need of quality improvement. Finally, unmet spiritual needs indicated by "religious struggles" (eg: feeling punished or deserted by God) are a predictor of increased mortality among medical patients following hospital discharge.'

So personal coping skills, decision making about treatments, community support in illness, and health outcomes are all associated with religious beliefs and practice. Religious beliefs feed into health beliefs. Where there is unmet spiritual need, as indicated by religious or existential struggles, there are worse health outcomes.

PUBLISHED STUDIES ON RELIGION AND HEALTH

The evidence for these associations has been explored in numerous research studies. Here it is not possible to explore the large body of literature [41] on the subject but some idea of the evidence is useful.

Studies correlating spirituality with improved health outcomes have now included a very wide range of diseases: heart disease, cancer, pain and depression. For example, in a study of gynaecological cancers 93% of patients said that religion helped sustain their hopes. [42]

Robert Hummer, of the University of Texas, and his colleagues followed the health of church attenders and matched controls over nine years: there were more than 20,000 subjects in the study. [43] Taking socioeconomic differences and health selection effects into account, they found that those who never attended services had twice the risk of dying in the next eight years compared with regular attenders. Overall there was a seven year difference in life expectancy at age 20 between the most frequent and least frequent attenders. There was a positive effect on all causes of death, though the magnitude of benefit varied with different causes. The group of people with occasional attendance had an intermediate risk profile. Correlation doesn't prove causality and they postulate that many subtle variables are at play, because even when they controlled for all known variables a beneficial effect was still present.

Daniel Hall of the University of Pittsburgh Medical Center found that church attendance accounted for 2-3 years' additional life.[44] Neal Krause of the University of Michigan found that a sense of gratitude predicts for less depression, and a sense of meaning predicts health.[45] Some of the possible links between religion and health are suggested in these studies. For example faith can motivate people to adopt healthier lifestyles; as when Christians see their bodies as no longer their own possession but as belonging to God and then as temples of the Holy Spirit. Gary McCord *et al* quoted previous studies showing that religious faith correlated with 'reduced morbidity and mortality, better physical and mental health, healthier lifestyles, fewer required health services, improved coping skills, enhanced well-being, reduced stress, and illness prevention'.[46]

Because there are so many worldviews, one would expect that similar studies to those reported from Ohio or those mentioned by Harold Koenig might reach different results in different countries. There are certainly fewer studies readily available outside the USA.

A study of over 8,000 people across five European countries showed a reduced prevalence of depression in regular church attendees, an effect most evident in Catholics.[47] In a study from University College London, Kiri Walsh *et al* studied grief in those with dying relatives who were followed up after bereavement and found that 'people who profess stronger spiritual beliefs seem to resolve their grief more rapidly and completely after the death of a close person than do people with no spiritual beliefs'.[48]

Also in London, Michael King and Gerard Leavey suggest that psychiatrists need to take greater account of patients' beliefs simply because 'there is abundant evidence that spiritual belief, experience and practice gives meaning to many people'.[49]

A GP'S STORY

Michael, a 63 year old, was a new diabetic. 'If it's OK by you, I'd rather not take the tablets for my diabetes.' When I enquired why, Michael explained that he belonged to a particular religious sect, and he believed that by faith he could be cured of his diabetes. As I knew next to nothing about this religion, he kindly lent me a book on the subject and readily agreed that we monitor his diabetes with blood tests to see how he got on.

We met at various intervals and the tests showed a steady deterioration over the months until we arrived at a time for further decisions. He asked me what I thought of the book and I explained how I felt its stance insulted God. I suggested that by God's gift we had discovered some of the wonders of his world, including some amazing medicines, and it seemed to me ungrateful to God not to take advantage of the blessings of this knowledge. What this required from Michael was a new faith in God's goodness in history and the opportunity to stop feeling falsely guilty that his own faith wasn't strong enough to cure his diabetes without medicines.

With tremendous humility he accepted these comments and started out on medication. In fact he became a very careful medicine taker. Previously I would have said he had become a compliant patient – but that is paternalistic – so perhaps 'concordant' is a better word. Once I had tapped into Michael's worldview and was willing to challenge it, he was more 'concordant' with the treatment and did very well.

Many years have passed since then and we have a warm and continued relationship; we certainly share a faith in God. I can see his faith has grown, but at present have no further insights into how his knowledge of God has developed. Whenever we meet he leaves me with a sincere 'God bless you' and as I return the blessing he tries hard to press some 'spice' (an old Yorkshire term for sweets) into my hand. These are usually a highly calorific humbug not entirely suited to diabetic diets! Perhaps I should have said he was 'slightly more concordant'!

Enquiry about a patient's worldview gives important insights into their understanding of their illness, their decision making strategies, their likely concordance with treatment and the community supports they are part of. Dietary issues become clear – for example, there is no point prescribing a three times daily medication during the fasting month to a Muslim (and often the Muslim patient will be far too polite to point out the difficulty), or a medication which is not *halal* or *kosher* (for example a calcium and vitamin D preparation which includes pork-derived gelatin).

The patient is often grateful when a clinician takes the trouble to enquire and clarify how the patient's worldview will affect the whole management of their illness, even pre-empting difficulties with good problem solving. It demonstrates an interest in the whole person and can improve trust. But because of the tremendous range of belief and practice it is wise not to jump to conclusions too quickly, or you can create difficulty where there is none!

PATIENTS WISH TO DISCUSS WORLDVIEW WITH CLINICIANS

Evidence that patients wish to have these discussions with their physicians came from the study of clinic attenders in north east Ohio.[50] Of 921 respondents, 83% wanted their physicians to ask about spiritual beliefs, while 17% did not. 'The most acceptable scenarios for spiritual discussion were life-threatening illnesses (77%), serious medical conditions (74%) and loss of loved ones (70%). Among those who wanted to discuss spirituality, the most important reason for discussion was desire for physician-patient understanding (87%). Patients believed that information concerning their spiritual beliefs would affect physicians' ability to encourage realistic hope (67%), give medical advice (66%), and change medical treatment (62%).'

It is important to note in this context that it is the physician's understanding that the patient seeks, not a chaplain's counsel. Referral to a religious 'expert' for counsel may be appropriate at another time, but here the patient wants their faith to be part of the equation in considering this illness. This is such an important point. It may well be that referral or self-referral onwards for counsel is often wise, and an important part of the management of a person's illness, but it is the role of the theologically non-expert healthcare professional we are primarily focusing on here.

A GP's STORY

A 32 year old man came to see me with his girlfriend. He hadn't slept since his younger brother's death by suicide while under the influence of illicit ketamine. He felt guilty that he hadn't warned his brother in stronger terms over the dangers of the drug. He found concentration difficult. Because of distance and impaired relationships with other family members he was unable to attend the funeral or even visit the grave. I asked, 'May I ask, do you have a religious faith?' to which came the reply 'I believe in God, but I don't go to church'. Following this we were able to discuss what he felt would be his brother's and God's views of his sense of guilt.

The pathways by which religious faith benefits health are apparently multiple and complex. Apart from more obvious impacts on lifestyle factors, fascinating links between attendance at religious services and interleukin-6 levels have been found and replicated. [51] If we know that religious faith is associated with better health, even if we don't fully understand by what pathway, it would seem that making patients aware of this could become an obligation rather than an option. In an increasingly litigious atmosphere, perhaps we will see the day when a clinician is sued for *not* mentioning the associated health benefits of religion! It is paradoxical in the extreme that Anand Rao, a bank staff nurse in Leicester, was dismissed in May 2009. [52] He had suggested church attendance as a beneficial idea to a colleague who was acting the part of a patient in a *simulation* training session!

From an evolutionary theory viewpoint it would be unsurprising if religion had some survival benefits (because it has not been selected out), while from a theistic viewpoint it would be expected that living according to the maker's instructions is beneficial to the individual and community. In this area worldview can affect research funding and publication bias. Research into religion and health can be used to try to validate or attack a particular worldview. [53]

THE NEGATIVE EFFECTS OF RELIGION ON PHYSICAL HEALTH

In addition to the wealth of evidence of benefit to health from the majority of religious practice, there are also the clearly negative effects on health of some forms of religion. Religion may be deleterious to physical health. It doesn't take a research paper to realise the effect of a suicide cult. And it also doesn't take much imagination to understand that if the patient before you is a member of a suicide cult, it would be a remarkably important piece of information to know.

Rather more commonly, patients identify guilt, shame, doubt or some sense of letting God down in association with their illness. It is just as significant to elicit the negative effects of worldview as it is to discover the positive possibilities. Patients can also feel that illness is a punishment, or is simply deeply unjust.

A GP'S STORY

A 22 year old woman presented some months after suffering false imprisonment, threats of death and finally rape. She emphasised several times that she couldn't get out of her mind just how unjust it was that it had happened to her, that she didn't deserve it. It made her realise that her worldview included a deep sense of justice. She rationalised that if it hadn't been her it would have been someone else, who might not have survived at all. She took some comfort that the attackers had been convicted.

There is also the caution that the search for truth, or the application of truth itself can place people's lives in danger from religious persecution, even in countries where there is freedom of speech and conscience.

A UK BASED DOCTOR'S STORY

One of my patients from an ethnic minority group attended the surgery about a minor illness. She was calm and serene in a way that she'd never been before. I commented on this and asked her what had happened. 'I've met Jesus' was her reply. Not long after this she was attacked by some young men from her community who had heard of her conversion.

It is also not surprising that if religious faith motivates someone to campaign against entrenched immorality, for example against pollution, trade injustice, poor working conditions, slavery, drug cartels and so forth, then they will find themselves up against powerful vested interests who will defend their evildoing with violence. If religion truly inspires self-sacrificial love, preservation of the adherent's health will not necessarily be their first priority.

So, research which looks at various aspects of health and religion in stable communities may miss other startling effects. It is also entirely possible for religious faith to have a dual effect, eg to benefit mood, while at the same time having a negative effect on life expectancy.

A SURGEON'S STORY

Once when I was working in south east Asia a beautiful old lady came to the surgical clinic with a large ulcerated cancer of her right cheek. It was about 5cm in diameter. I was the most senior local surgeon at the time and, surrounded by medical students, was her only hope of treatment. I advised her that treatment would mean travel to the capital city for the surgery and radiotherapy she needed.

We could arrange transport for the ten hour journey and accommodation for the family there. She studied me serenely for a moment. I could see I might as well have asked her to fly to the moon. Already, coming to see me was the longest journey she had ever made in her life. She had never before left her home region. She was a Muslim and had been taught to accept without doubts God's timing for her death, and she would have major concerns about interfering unnaturally with that process. And anyway such a big decision was always made by the community getting together for a debate to arrive at a consensus, not by an individual acting alone.

Her reply to my offer was simple: 'Balik kampung'. ('I'll go back to the village.') My language was limited; I felt desperate for her as I could guess how this might end. All I could do was hold her hands in mine and say, 'Makcik, kita semua dalam tangan Tuhan' ('Aunty, we are all in the hands of the Lord'). She replied 'Macam Surat' ('That is like a promise from the Q'uran'). She did not come back to the clinic.

FINDING COMMON GROUND
BETWEEN CLINICIAN AND PATIENT

In this last story I wonder whether you think the impact of worldview on the illness was negative or positive. One thing that it does clearly illustrate is that important point: patients appreciate being understood (as the Ohio research suggested). It would not be surprising if this, at least, is applicable across the world. As in this case, common ground between patient and healthcare worker can build trust and help develop the therapeutic relationship.

If, for example, both nurse and patient support the same football team a brief comment about the team's recent performance is a way of sharing our common humanity. It gives the patient a sense of shared community. So if a doctor shares an experience of bringing up his or her own children to illustrate a possible intervention for a patient, especially emphasising the mistakes made, the patient may feel more comfortable with the suggested course of action regarding the management of her own children. The more intensely a particular interest is held by the patient, the higher the value placed on any discovered commonality. The converse can be true too: 'That midwife didn't understand what it's like, she's not had children of her own'.

This is not to say that the clinician has to have been through everything before being able to express empathy. Rather it is that we can learn to use the totality of who we are for the patient's benefit. Expressed with a humble awareness of not being in the other person's shoes, our experiences can add to directly expressed empathy as a source of comfort. So when the patient and clinician discover they share a faith, a very significant extra bond in the therapeutic relationship is formed, with the freedom to include a faith perspective in the shared understanding of the illness and treatment.

A PATIENT'S STORY

I shared some parts of my difficulties with my doctor, who is a Christian. This has made it easier to go to the doctors to get help for depression. God is very good at putting the right people in the right places.

A GP's STORY

I am often surprised at what patients have done about their illnesses before consulting me, when I take the trouble to enquire. It often amounts to considerably more than a trial of paracetamol or some advice from the family. On one occasion Ahmed, a 35 year old originally from the Horn of Africa, attended troubled by his 'voices'. The voices were male, generally derogatory and seemed to come from outside.

When I asked what he thought about the voices and where they came from he said he didn't know. But when I then asked whether he thought they might be spirits of some sort he replied, 'Exactly!' If he thought they were spirits, had he done anything about it? Yes indeed, he had visited the Imam who had read the Q'uran and prayed for him, but he had not found it helpful.

Later in the consultation I was then able to explain that as a Christian I believed in spirits and in Jesus' power over them, but also that brain chemistry could go wrong and produce similar symptoms and that God had given us some powerful medications to help. He was pleased I had addressed his worldview and accepted the medication and onward referral. When I discussed Ahmed with a Muslim colleague she was entirely unsurprised by his resort to the Imam as first port of call.

Larry Culliford, a psychiatrist, suggested that spirituality can be compared with nutrition in healthcare: 'neither is a subject that healthcare providers can take for granted'. [54] This is because the consequences of ignoring nutrition are costly in terms of susceptibility to disease and delayed recovery. He stated in 2002 that evidence was steadily mounting that this also held for 'spiritual sustenance'.

HELPING PATIENTS UNDERSTAND THE WORLDVIEW OF THOSE CLOSE TO THEM

Sometimes the history taking reveals a worldview difference between the patient and people important to them, which can then be used to help the patient. Take, for example:

A GP's Story

A businessman was very distressed. His father, after a long depressive illness, had committed suicide some weeks previously. The businessman felt guilty because the family had argued strongly for the discharge from the mental hospital, and then shortly after coming home his father had taken his own life. What particularly upset him was that he couldn't speak to his wife about his feelings or the pressures he was under at work. He was also trying to start sorting out his father's considerable financial debts.

I realised that his wife was from a more formally Buddhist background where it was not usual to verbalise emotional difficulties with those close to you. I tentatively suggested that apart from her own sadness, her view of the nature and problem of suffering might differ from his, as a very westernised Asian. She might not find it easy to empathise with his difficulties. When he returned for follow up he commented how useful this analysis had been, and how it had helped their relationship and his handling of the grief.

Worldview is such a critical aspect of a patient's global understanding that the elucidation of it in history taking should not be haphazard. It is one thing to discover that a patient prefers lemon to fruit flavoured tablets, but it is another thing altogether to discover that their religion forbids them from taking the medication in the first place. Liberating our medical curiosity with open questions and some lateral thinking will hopefully prevent pointless interventions and open up therapeutic options not previously considered.

4. SPIRITUAL HISTORY TAKING

In many parts of the world a patient is asked their religion on admission to hospital. The next question being 'Who is your next of kin?' makes you feel that religion is all about dying and it wouldn't be a surprise if the final question was 'Which would you prefer – burial or cremation?'

In the UK the entry in the notes on religion may be looked at again if the patient is dying, but otherwise tends to be ignored. Healthcare workers don't usually ask the question, and might even be embarrassed to ask 'What is your religion?' I think this is a comment on the state of our society rather than anything else. When I travelled in India the first question to me as a fellow passenger on a train was often 'What is your religion?' while in Kenya the first question was often 'Have you been born again?' There was no shame at all in asking immediately about the cornerstone of your life – your worldview; in fact it was polite to do so. But currently in the UK, speaking to a stranger about their religion is almost more taboo than talking about death!

So it isn't surprising that medical staff and patients in the UK or USA may feel uncomfortable. Jean Kristeller of Indiana State University found oncologists willing but feeling under equipped to broach spiritual questions. [55] She has gone on to trial brief 'spiritual' interventions by oncologists and oncology nurses which have been well received. [56]

A DOCTOR'S STORY

I've never been rebuffed, so it makes me wonder if I'm too cautious, but I think I normally have a sense of when it is appropriate to discuss faith. I was working in the Accident and Emergency Department when a man was admitted with severe chest pain. I realised he had a dissecting aortic aneurysm and prepared him for surgery, arranging the blood for cross match. While I was getting him ready he said, 'I have had a wonderful life'. I didn't know how to respond. He died on the operating table. I was congratulated for good and prompt organisation but have always regretted that I was too afraid to respond to his comment.

The sensible time for worldview to be assessed is at patient registration or first attendance, and it can fit naturally into an expanded social history. Patients' desire to speak of spirituality with their doctors increases with the seriousness of the illness. In the Ohio study already mentioned, McCord and colleagues found that 43% of patients wished to talk about spirituality on their initial visit to a doctor, but that if a life threatening illness had just been diagnosed this climbed to 77%. [57] For those suffering grief over the loss of a loved one the figure was 70%. Their study suggests that a screening question would identify *with increasing probability* those who would welcome a discussion. Health record systems need to include space for some notes on world view and implications for care – provided confidentiality is adequately protected.

Sometimes the herbs, potions, over the counter remedies and prayers that people have tried before coming to you will give useful clues about their worldview. But it is not just what people say that gives you important clues.

USING NON-VERBAL CUES

Understanding a patient's worldview can start before a word is spoken. We are trained to look out for the non-verbal cues that lead to a diagnosis and in the same way there are often signs of a patient's worldview. How they dress, for example:

A GP'S STORY

Julie, a 34 year old lady, attended with symptoms of acid reflux ('heartburn'), for which she had tried some 'herbal remedies'. Her naturally dyed loose clothes, her general manner and the comment 'vegetarian' in the notes gave me some further ideas. Once we had gone over her symptoms and the examination was normal, I actually felt a bit mischievous when I suggested 'How about some seaweed?'

She was surprised and pleased as I explained that the alginate in a common remedy for heartburn is derived from seaweed. She accepted the advice with enthusiasm. I went on to explain that a large number of modern medicines are derived from nature, but couldn't resist a mild dig about avoiding some naturally occurring poisonous chemicals!

Several useful questions have been devised to open up the subject of worldview. In the useful course *International Saline* [58] a question that is suggested (and very usable) is the one the doctor used with Fred in Chapter 2: 'Do you have a faith to support you at a time like this?' Patients answering in the affirmative usually expand their answer naturally, while patients replying 'No' often say so in a manner that suggests they have no desire to talk about that and the history taking can move on.

Another useful question is that suggested by Daniel Sulmasy in his book *The Healer's Calling*: [59] 'What role does religion play in your life?' If patients pause or look uncomfortable or mystified or ask why this question is being asked, then an explanatory comment such as 'faith can have a big impact on how people handle illness' will put the patient at ease.

I have tried questions such as 'Why do you think this might be happening in your life?' but patients usually respond with physical or psychological causes because they think that's what I want to hear, which I do, but it isn't quite what I am trying to get at! They won't respond with 'Because God is punishing me' unless they know it's OK to speak of such things.

A PHYSICIAN'S STORY

One thing I do after I've broken bad news to a patient is ask, 'Have you anybody to talk to, who you could tell about it? A relative, a friend, a vicar?'

I suppose this story is revealing in that the patients of that doctor were likely to know what a vicar was – most of my patients would have no idea! My mother, a GP, once asked a patient (who had been a prostitute for many years) 'Do you ever think about God?' to which came the reply, 'I think about him all the time'. My mother's preconceived ideas were demolished in a second. A deep and thoughtful conversation ensued. One respiratory physician I came across always looks at the chart to see what had been indicated in the 'religion' slot. Working in the UK she found that some abbreviations such as 'RC' [60] generally indicated an active faith, but some of her most interesting conversations happened with patients who had a line drawn across that section.

'FICA'

The George Washington University website [61] has a course on spiritual history taking based on the validated 'FICA' tool. [62]

$$\underline{FICA}$$

F : FAITH / BELIEFS
I : IMPORTANCE / IMPACT
C : COMMUNITY
A : ACTION

'F' is for Faith/belief/meaning and suggested questions might include 'Do you have faith, beliefs, a religious outlook that gives you comfort, encouragement, or help?' or 'Describe what gives your life meaning.'

A GYNAECOLOGIST'S STORY

In the UK a lot of people will put down C of E [63] *as their religion but it often means very little to them practically, so I ask people 'Is faith in God something that is important to you?'*

The 'I' in FICA is for importance: 'How might your beliefs impact your health decisions?' or 'If something happened and you were unable to express what you wanted, is there someone you'd trust to represent your beliefs in decision making?'

'C' is for community – 'Are you part of a faith community?' or 'Is there a group of people who are especially important to you?' or 'Do you have a religious leader/pastor/priest?'

'A' is for address (actions agreed) flowing from this part of the history, for example referral to a chaplaincy, etc.

A GP'S STORY

One of my patients, a 70 year old man, had successful surgery for a cancer. It had been a quick story from diagnosis to surgery, and now suddenly post-operatively he had some time to think. He was having some sleeping difficulty and anxiety episodes as his frailty struck him. His children had reminded him that he was beginning to get old. We discussed the wound discomfort, his relationships and the supports he had and then I asked, 'Have you a religious faith?' 'Yes' he said calmly, 'Church of England'. There was a pause. 'I'm an orphan, you see, both my parents died when I was six, maybe that's where my anxiety really comes from ...'

And he went on to describe the good and bad things about the strict religious orphanage where he was brought up; the things he was grateful for and the things that he'd been told to be grateful for, but wasn't. He'd married and raised a family with great affection and now enjoyed his grandchildren.

I was so glad to get this tremendous insight into this man's life. 'What an amazing story' I said, 'Through everything, the ups and downs, despite the lack of physical affection in the orphanage, it

> *seems to me that you have felt you were looked after and you still
> have faith'. 'Yes' he said, 'That's right'. I was then able to reassure
> him that he was experiencing a normal reaction to his illness, and
> he decided he didn't want any medication for the present.*

Mention of faith or religion can be a trigger to an area of experience
that the patient wasn't otherwise going to talk about. On this occasion
it would appear there was time to listen and then the opportunity to
affirm the experience. It enabled the patient to explore the physical,
psychological, social and spiritual context for the present anxiety.
The trigger is not always comfortable and can raise painful memories
of disappointment with the bad behaviour of 'religious' people.

'HOPE'

The HOPE tool [64] is fairly similar to the FICA tool.

HOPE

H : SOURCES OF HOPE / MEANING
O : ROLE OF ORGANISED RELIGION
P : PERSONAL PRACTICE OF BELIEFS
E : EFFECT OF BELIEFS ON MEDICAL DECISIONS

'H' is asking about sources of hope, meaning, comfort, strength, peace
or love in a patient's life. 'O' is asking about the role of organised
religion. 'P' is asking about personal spiritual beliefs and practice.
'E' is enquiry about the effects of these beliefs in medical choice,
coping, and end of life decisions.

Placing the enquiry within the social history is often unthreatening to
a patient. So questions such as 'What do you do to maintain a healthy
lifestyle?' and 'What are your recreations?' could very naturally be
followed by 'Do you attend a place of worship?' or 'Are you involved
in any faith community?' or 'Tell me about your spiritual beliefs'.

A GP'S STORY

I find it helpful to have certain cues that make me consider whether a question about faith would be useful to the patient. For example, as a city centre practice we have a high turnover, so there is a steady stream of new patients. As anyone who lives in a big city knows, the biggest problem, ironically, is loneliness. So my main question to new arrivals is how they will build friendships and new social networks. A good social network has major implications for personal health (and how appropriately people use the health services!)

I usually ask how they intend to make friends locally and they usually haven't planned it. The range of ideas the patients present is always fascinating. If there are none I enquire about their work, family, interests, hobbies, sports and faith. I can often point them in the direction of a good gym or a walking club or whatever. Then I might ask: 'May I say something personal from my experience?' If they say 'yes', I may go on to say how my wife and I arrived in the city knowing no one and how, because of getting involved in a church, we had friends who had stuck by us through thick and thin. They often respond by saying that they wouldn't go to a church purely for social reasons, and I say that it was fine to go for social reasons, they don't have to join in the bits they don't believe, but it might give them an opportunity to explore more of what life is all about.

Questions don't always have to be formulaic, and triggers for a patient to discuss their worldview often come out of the blue. One doctor told me of a remarkable exchange with a patient, who was struggling with addiction, which was opened with the question from the doctor: 'Can a leopard change his spots?'

Oblique questions in some cultures can be more polite and effective, especially where a direct question about involvement in religious practice might suggest criticism (eg 'Do you attend mosque regularly?' which could be seen to mean 'You should do, but I doubt it').

A GP TRAINER'S STORY

A thoughtful Muslim couple had come to discuss a request for termination of pregnancy. The main issue seemed to be their financial worries. As I explored their fears about their future finances, I said 'Have you ever been hungry or not had a roof or clothes?' to which came the reply from the husband, 'I know what you're getting at – no; God has always given us what we needed'. 'So do you think you could you trust him to provide for this little one?' They thought they could, and, in the event, they did.

My registrar was sitting in on this consultation. Afterwards as we reflected together, my registrar upbraided me that I was not their Imam, with which I was happy to agree! After 'a robust exchange of views' I did point out that it was our duty to have a bias to our more vulnerable or voiceless patients and advocate for them, and that in this case the baby needed an advocate who could wield arguments that would register with the parents.

A GP'S STORY

A 37 year old school teacher attended, six weeks pregnant. She had a partner of five years and explained that they had had no intention of having children. During a recent viral illness she had suffered vomiting and thought that was why the contraceptive pill had failed as she had been regular in taking it.

She described their complete state of uncertainty as to how to proceed. Should she request a termination of pregnancy or proceed with the pregnancy? We discussed her social situation, the possibility of redundancy from work for her partner, and then the medical pros and cons of proceeding with pregnancy. Then I said 'The medical and social issues in this are all important, but actually they are probably a small factor because what will really help you are your ethical views, your worldview, what you think about God and so on'.

She looked pleasantly surprised. 'I'm so glad you said that' she replied. 'Is it really ethical to bring a child into our world when climate change is likely to cause so much suffering in the future and the population is already growing so fast?' 'You are right – these are huge issues, and there are other children whose welfare it is good to keep in mind.'

> *I then added, 'When you came into the room, I noticed that you were nervous and also seemed excited. The urge to be a parent is strong. I suggest you go and talk these issues over with your partner and come back in a few days. You will know that we are a practice with a Christian ethos and so we are not in favour of abortion; but we will be here for you whatever you decide.' As she was leaving she again thanked me for exploring things with her.*

Patients need to be very free not to have discussions of their worldview if they don't want to, and watching for visual and verbal cues to back off is important. This is the same pattern as in any intimate enquiry – for example, a sexual history. There may be many reasons why the patient would rather not speak about it, and we'll explore some of these in Chapter 19.

Being curious, I would like to know why the patient closes down this area of discussion, as that in itself may lead to important understanding. Opportunity may then present itself later to ask gently, 'We know that a patient's worldview can affect how they handle illness and I noticed that you seemed upset when I asked whether faith was important to you. I'm sorry if I upset you and I was wondering why that was? You don't need to talk about it if you don't want to.' Ask this sort of a question in as open a way as possible and never prejudge the answer in advance.

One among the many possibilities is that the patient never considered that it might be relevant. Considering worldview as not applicable in medical encounters is especially prevalent in a form of dualism.

AT A GIVEN MOMENT

5. A FORM OF DUALISM – 'THE SACRED/SECULAR DIVIDE'

When Caroline Petrie, a community nurse, was warned about offering prayer cards to patients in 2008,[65] her boss wrote to her saying: 'As a nurse you are required to uphold the reputation of your profession. Your NMC [Nursing and Midwifery Council] code states that "you must demonstrate a personal and professional commitment to equality and diversity" and "you must not use your professional status to promote causes that are not related to health"'.

When one considers the impact of worldview on health it is difficult to see which of these she was breaching. The underlying assumption is that worldview has no relationship to health, or to patient/professional interactions. Any expression which could be deemed to reflect a worldview might be suspect. If this line of thinking is taken to its conclusion then even saying 'What a beautiful day' to a patient could be risky – a value judgment imposing a particular view of the weather!

In this type of dualism is the idea that the material and spiritual are separate realms with little or no relationship between them. [66,67,68] Following the Enlightenment, supernatural reasons for events were gradually sidelined, as strict scientific cause and effect became the basis of an understanding of the world. Spiritual explanations became progressively a separate matter, and increasingly privatised as not holding objectively verifiable reality. So rather than being centrally integrated in the culture in the United Kingdom, faith has been gradually marginalised.

An example of this is plainly seen in the media where faith is separated into a minority interest and is compartmentalised. This gradual dissociation of our culture from God is patchy. We have the same national anthem invoking God, we remember our dead at the Cenotaph with prayers, and we continually appeal to law and morality which have a basis in Christian philosophy and ethics. But we are increasingly excluding God from education, law, and hospitals despite 71% stating their religion as 'Christianity' in the latest UK household survey. [69]

The basic principles of free will and moral accountability upon which all human societies today function are not scientifically provable, but are derived from beliefs and the value systems which flow from them. This shows that we all live by faith; and that is by faith in our worldview. As Christians we believe that there is actually truth about the nature of creation which cannot be verified by science alone.

And everyone makes assumptions in their worldview and acts by faith. Consider a rope bridge across a deep gorge. Watching a heavy guide go across before you may help you develop the necessary faith. There will be no point saying, 'Oh, yes, I see now that bridge is fine', but refusing to cross! We live by thousands and thousands of small acts of faith every day. So the idea of leaving beliefs at the door of the consulting room is ludicrous for clinician or patient.

A GP's COMMENT [70]
Quite apart from rights and wrongs, it is impossible for doctors, or anyone else, not to pass on something of their attitude to life and the values they hold. It will show in everything they do.

And while a Christian clinician respects the autonomy of the patient, he or she doesn't collude with untruth, either about the disease or about the patient's erroneous worldview. The clinician knows his or her own fallibility both in medicine and faith and humbly listens to the patient's views, celebrating and seeking the truth together. But the point is that there is truth to be found. God has poured out truth generously and we learn truth in community.

THE ORIGINS OF THIS DUALISM

This sort of dualism has also infiltrated Christian thinking in the West. At its root the idea of dualism comes from Greek thinkers and has been adopted into Western Christianity partly through Descartes. [71] The idea that the body/material world is evil and the spiritual/unseen world is good has led to a spiritualisation of heaven by Christians. It is an understandable reaction to confusion over a suffering creation which was embraced centuries ago by the Gnostics.

The Bible knows no such distinction – in biblical thought God created the spiritual realm and the material world, and they are completely integrated into each other. The spiritual realm operates to laws no less than the material world, and it intersects with the material world. In the book of Job, a wealthy man suffers unjustly and brings his complaint to God. After listening to the accusations God replies. He challenges man, apparently playfully: 'Where were you when I laid the earth's foundation? Tell me if you understand.' [72] This challenge to understand and control the material world has been taken up (consciously and unconsciously) in a massive scientific research effort over the last 200 years. The result is that we know amazing things about the universe. But we have also found that for every question we answer there are many more questions. The 'God of the gaps' just got exponentially bigger.

God's challenge to Job has additional serious subtlety: if we cannot fully understand material phenomena, how can we fully grasp the reasons for suffering and what is going on in the unseen realms? It is perhaps natural that, faced with so much evil in the world, so much suffering, we sympathise naturally with the Platonic ideas and the material world comes to be seen as bad and the spiritual world and a disembodied life after death as good.

However, the Bible sees the Creation as good, although impacted and marred by man's evil, pride and selfishness and it anticipates a transformation of the material world in the future into which the kings of the earth bring their splendour. In this future, suffering is abolished. Evil is banished. For God does not abandon relationships he has made. Heaven comes to earth.

A GP's STORY

Recently, one lady returned to me with her depression much improved. No, she had not taken the medication, but – and she said she knew I would disapprove – she had consulted a medium and had a comforting message from her deceased mother. I encouraged her to describe the experience to me. And why did she think I would disapprove? Because she knew I was a Christian. I agreed that the Bible advised strongly against the practice of consulting mediums, but said I was glad she had not needed the medication and had found comfort.

We don't need to compromise our worldview to work with patients. Do you think the doctor did that in this example? If we blandly affirm people's personal beliefs we become disconnected from them, implicitly denying that there is any reality to be found in spiritual ideas, but merely wish fulfilment. Surely it is better to be co-travellers on a journey to seek the truth together; the truth about the disease and the truth about life's meaning.

This doesn't mean ramming the truth as we see it down people's throats. We know for ourselves that we can usually only take a little of the truth about ourselves at one time, so if a patient doesn't want to hear the truth about anything, including their disease, we need to sense that, and approach with gentleness and sensitivity.

DUALISM AND THE CONSULTATION

We see the sacred/secular divide in everyday life. In the British media, religious issues are boxed into specifically religious programmes, whereas all other issues are discussed together. Where religion figures, for example in a 'soap', it is as an add-on and its impact on 'real' life is rarely mentioned. With religious jargon in speech among themselves, Christians can perpetuate this idea. Religion comes to be seen as an optional extra of little relevance to daily life, and of interest only to a few with an inclination that way, a hobby.

So it is not surprising that those without a religious worldview think that talk of a clinician's faith should usually be excluded from consultations, and that religious discussions should be left to 'the experts'. It would be like enduring a lecture on some esoteric branch of philately before you were allowed to sign a consent form to have your hernia repaired – time wasting and irrelevant.

What has all this to do with us and consultations? The answer is that our worldview as western Christians has been deeply influenced by our culture, so that we have an inherent discomfort speaking of faith matters and integrating faith into our speech and lives. We may have been through a higher educational system that by and large ignores God. How do these ideas permeate into meetings with patients?

DUALISM AND CHRISTIAN CLINICIANS

Dualistic Christians tend to react in two ways. First, the dualistic doctor may say that his Christian faith should not be expressed verbally in consultations. It is, as it were, a private part of his life and while informing his values and morals the doctor would not feel comfortable expressing it to colleagues or patients. This approach would be supported by secular society in some western countries and completely mystify people in other cultures. Christians, and that includes Christians in medicine, need to break out of this mould.

Christians believe that the eternal destiny of each person depends on their response to God's offer of free forgiveness through Jesus Christ's death and resurrection. This creates a natural urgency and passion to spread the good news of this offer with Jesus' call to 'make disciples'. This results in a second problem for some dualistic Christians. They see the medical work fundamentally as a tool to enable them to do the really important work of explaining Christian faith. For them, saving souls from this vale of tears is really all that counts. They have a hierarchy of tasks. Medical work is good but secondary. It is an access tool or even just a financial milk cow that will pay for the most important work: gospel proclamation.

These people may be the best clinicians in the world, but feel that unless they are speaking of their faith they are letting God down.

I remember a colleague who told me that a mission hospital had to decide what it was about: it had to choose between evangelism and health care. At the time I really didn't understand his problem. Looking back I realise it was the false choice presented by a dualistic worldview. Love involves embodying and expressing truth. Being 'salt and light'. For the Christian this means timely action and timely explanation. The question is what does God want me to be doing now: still or active, silent or speaking? As the book of Ecclesiastes reminds me, there is a time for everything. [73] And you can see that I have slipped quietly back into the individualistic culture from which I spring even as I consider this! The question should be: what does God want us to be doing, and what is my role in that, with the individual gifts given to me as part of the church, 'the body of Christ'? [74]

What will this look like in practice? At different times we will be planning access to clinics, allowing patients space to be heard, keeping ourselves up to date, developing research, teaching, ensuring fair employment terms for staff, being honest with clinic finances, ensuring we minimise our environmental impact *and* being ready to share the hope we have: our whole lives, including rest, offered as worship.

A GP's STORY

I work in a practice with a longstanding Christian ethos. We had a discussion at the practice meeting as to whether we could have Christian magazines in the waiting room. Part of the discussion centred on whether it was right to force a worldview on our patients at a possibly vulnerable time in their lives. One riposte was 'You mean that the other magazines we have, like Vogue, Good Housekeeping and Country Life, don't have a message?'

We may have many roles in our complex society, but we don't stop being a parent, sibling, employer, student, taxpayer, customer or worshipper when we enter the consulting room or the hospital ward. By all means focus on the task in hand but don't leave your humanity or faith outside the door.

6. THE CONCEPT OF 'FAITH FLAGS'

A GP'S STORY

I was working as a locum GP. On the bookshelf in sight of the patient was a Bible. As a part of their story the patient said, 'I noticed you have a Bible on the shelf and I was wondering...'

There are many ways in which a patient discovers that they can be safe and comfortable discussing faith issues with their doctor. One is that the doctor takes a spiritual history, or offers a discussion around a spiritual history already noted in the records. Another is by the natural mention of 'faith flags'. A faith flag might even be as simple as the doctor being known to be a Christian. One friend described it to me as being as gentle as floating some crumbs on the surface of a pool of water and watching to see if the fish bites.

Just being known as a Christian can have surprising effects. One patient attended the local church for the first time. The vicar enquired what had brought him to church and he explained that his GP had shaken hands with him and welcomed him at the surgery and it was the first time in his life anyone had treated him with dignity. He knew the GP was a Christian and so here he was. It is not clear just how the patient knew.

Signalling to the patient that 'God talk' is OK

In our practice it was several years before the bulk of our recently arrived Somali patients realised we were Christians. We had a plaque on the wall saying that the building had been opened 'to the Glory of God', but as the three male doctors all had beards, it had been assumed initially that we were Jews![75] I hope we didn't let Judaism down too much during that time! Knowing of our Christian faith, many of them have said how they pray for the success of our work in the clinic. That is a very generous expression of their gratitude.

Doubt is sinful in some religions, so some patients may feel much happier sharing their doubts with someone of another faith or none because they will feel less judged. I've had patients who have sought me as a God-fearer because they feel they won't be laughed at when they discuss evil spirits, or even to seek my opinion as to whether their experiences are spiritual or psychotic. The key is a warm welcome, a gentle patient-centred approach which is respectful but honest.

If a Bible on a shelf is one clue to a patient, then an apt quotation from the Bible is another.

An opthalmologist's faith flag
After I have instilled some drops into a patient's eye and wiped away the excess, I sometimes say 'He will wipe every tear from their eyes'. Sometimes the patient picks up on the comment and sometimes not.

A doctor's story
At the end of a consultation I looked at the elderly lady and said, 'Well, Mum, you're of more value than many sparrows'. 'Ooh!' she replied, 'I haven't heard that one for years!' 'And you've been paying your taxes for it too!' said I.

What faith flags might work for you and your patients? Any mention of church, God, Christian friends, faith or prayer will signal to the patient that you are comfortable to talk about these things. And word gets around the community of patients and staff. In a family medicine setting it is quite easy to get a reputation as one who is willing to speak about

Jesus if the patient wishes it, and a reputation as one who holds God-fearing with honour even at the same time as not showing disrespect to anyone.

What is appropriate as a faith flag will vary according to your culture and context. For example, currently in the UK an apt quotation from the Bible, a mention of prayer, or parting words such as 'God bless you' may be appropriate in certain circumstances. After all, 'Goodbye' is merely the shortened form of 'God be with you'.

A HOSPITAL DOCTOR'S STORY

I invited the lady into the consulting room. 'And how are you?' I enquired. 'Not in a bad state, thank you' she replied. So I said, 'As my mother used to say, "I'm not too bad considering the state I'm in"'. She smiled and let this pass without comment and the consultation proceeded amicably. As we were ending she asked me, 'Is your mother still alive?' 'No, she died eight years ago.' 'Oh, I'm sorry.' 'It's alright; she knew where she was going.' There was a comfortable pause, and then we finished off the consultation.

An awareness of the likely emotional state of the patient in certain circumstances and being sensitive to that are helpful.

AN ANAESTHETIST'S STORY

Patients are frequently rather nervous when they come into the operating theatre. In the anaesthetic room there is usually a short wait and often the patient says something like 'Do a good job, won't you?' or 'Good luck'. I will often reply with 'Well, I'm not doing it on my own' or a similar comment and indicate upwards. The patient often then comes out with a comment about how they go to church or say 'That's good'. And occasionally they will say 'Pray for me'.

AN OBSTETRICIAN'S STORY

I enjoy appreciating babies with their parents and frequently say, 'A baby is such a wonderful gift from God!' My Muslim patients like that very much and it gives me an immediate connection at another level with them.

AN OBSTETRICIAN'S STORY

*After delivery mothers are upset when they have a third degree tear
or a large episiotomy. They are often anxious about how it will
heal. 'It's a big tear, will it be OK?' I reply that God designed this
part of the body so that it would heal well, so we can be hopeful it
will. I have never had a negative response.*

A GP'S STORY

*I am forever advising my patients not to use cotton buds to clean
out their itching ears. It causes otitis externa. It is rather a negative
message, so I have tempered it with the time honoured adage:
'The smallest thing that you should put in your ear is your elbow'.
This usually at least raises a smile as the patient tries to do that.
More recently I've taken to saying 'It's there in God's design – even
the little finger won't go in'. And this is sometimes picked up
by the patient.*

A HOSPICE CHAPLAIN'S STORY

*Dying patient (or relative): 'I'm not religious'. My reply: 'Neither
am I! We can talk about anything you want.' I try to blow away
traditional ideas and misconceptions so that patients and relatives
feel safe. For example, a bereaved unbelieving husband and his five
year old daughter felt so safe that during the funeral she could
whisper what she wanted to say about her Mum in my ear and I
repeated it to the mourners. This was the product of time spent with
them at the hospice as her Mum died, and something of what they
saw in my life. In conversation I look out for hooks to hang
something on: if a relative or patient asks 'How will I cope?'
my reply might be: 'Being a Christian is what works for me'.*

VISUAL AND OTHER FAITH FLAGS

A MEDICAL STUDENT'S TALE

*I have the habit of wearing something that might be a talking point
for people. On this occasion I had a small fish badge. It was a
Friday evening and at the end of clerking an old lady on the ward,
she asked me: 'What does that fish mean?' 'It means I have faith in*

Jesus and the living God.' She wanted to talk about it and we had a brief chat, but I said I needed to hurry to catch the last train home, and we could continue on Monday if she wanted. She said she'd really like that and I rushed off.

On Monday I couldn't find her on the ward and asked the ward sister who informed me she'd died over the week-end. I have always felt a bit stupid about it – what did a train matter if she wanted me to stay and chat? I remember her and try to make the most of every opportunity.

Visual faith flags are commonly used. As in the story above, some wear the old Christian sign, the fish. *Icthus*, the Greek word for fish, was used as an acrostic with each letter the start of a word – in this case 'Jesus Christ, God's Son, Saviour'. I have used various pictures in my consulting room. One is of a shaft of sunlight catching a beautiful flower of paradise, a *Strelitzia*, against a black background. This has often brought comment and questions from patients. I tell them it reminds me of my patients and their illnesses – the hope of something remarkable happening in a dark place, or words to that effect, or to remind me that Jesus is a specialist at bringing good out of evil times. My response to their question would depend on them and varies a lot.

Similarly I have a picture that my Dad painted of his two hands. Depending on which way up the picture is, the hands are raised in supplication or downward in blessing. However, the position I usually have it is sideways, when the hands appear to be supporting or nurturing. This often brings positive comments, and patients like the fact it was my Dad who painted it; it gives them a sense of connectedness. It also gives them something to consider as I tap away at the computer or endeavour to extract an unwilling prescription from the jaws of the printer!

One doctor told me that he has a painting on the wall of a screwed up piece of paper – actually Psalm 119, which patients use as a conversation starter. Another has an African scene of the Prodigal Son's homecoming.

A DENTIST'S STORY

I've known many of my patients for more than 20 years. When I'm chatting with the nurses or patients my church activities or attendance at an interesting Bible study are naturally mentioned in the mix of things. I'm not afraid to talk about what I've been doing and I don't censor out these aspects of my life. Our family sponsors a child with Compassion UK[76] in Africa, and in the clinic, alongside photos of my children I have a photo of him. Patients are always asking me about my children and then come to the photo and ask, 'And who is this?'

Once I've explained they always want updates when they come for a check-up and so I update all the photos regularly too. It gives me a marvellous opportunity to speak of this work, and if they show great interest I point them to the film About Schmidt starring Jack Nicholson, about an accountant whose life falls apart after retirement but who then sponsors an African child. Also my children go to a school with a Christian ethos, and my patients often ask about that and why we chose that option.

It is remarkable how a small episode of humour, or a developing relationship over time with a clinician, can deepen a sense of connectedness. This doesn't take a lot of time and deepens our feeling of being part of a community. The patient is encouraged to reveal more of their concerns if they are aware of the bond of a common faith. Faith flags can trigger this process. Practitioners with an agnostic or atheistic world view can encourage patients to discuss these issues, not just by remembering to include a spiritual history, but by including supportive comments in the practice or hospital leaflets so that patients are encouraged to be bolder in sharing their deepest concerns. Of course some patients will try to use a stated commonality of worldview to try to manipulate or get a favour.

A GP'S STORY

Because we are known as a practice with a Christian ethos, patients occasionally try to manipulate us in the not so subtle style of 'You do know I'm a Christian too, don't you? Now can you give me the diazepam?' The obvious reply goes something along the lines of 'It's great you have a faith in Jesus because you'll understand that love must sometimes be tough'!

'A faith flag is a brief statement in the natural course of conversation that lets a patient know that you have spiritual resources to share.' [77] Faith flags may be objects, music, words, and pictures. Consider carefully what might be your flags.

A GP'S STORY

We tried some gentle Christian music in the waiting room but patients complained it was like going to a funeral – so we gave up on that!

And finally, it is worth remembering that the impact of faith flags can last a long time:

TWO DOCTORS' STORY

A married couple who were both doctors died after long and fruitful careers. They asked for a punch line of just five words on their gravestone: 'May Jesus Christ be praised'.

7. BUILDING TRUST

U sually in family medicine there is the opportunity to build trust over time and repeated consultations. But in many branches of medicine trust must be built rapidly so that an anxious patient and their family can feel safe and able to engage. For most patients every positive encounter with a team or staff member builds a certain amount of trust. It is rather as if, in winning the trust, the team and clinician are growing a credit account of trust much like a bank account.

The credit or debit starts with the ease of making the appointment, public transport, (or parking for bike or car), disabled access, the state of the clinic building, the warmth of the welcome at reception, and the quality of the waiting area, and that's just for starters! Then during the clinical encounter the patient will notice the quality of the listening, whether they feel heard and valued, whether a coherent formulation of the problem is achieved and a satisfactory plan made. Then there is the preparation for unplanned surprises in safety netting, and hopefully a cure. If the patient has a good experience of all these things then a credit balance of trust is created.

A GP'S STORY
A new patient, a 47 year old lady, came and requested that I set up her repeat medications. She told me of her problems. She had seen a number of doctors before and was on long term medication for

menopausal symptoms, depression, high blood pressure, obesity and dry skin. I simply listened. And then suggested we check her thyroid blood tests. I felt sad when she said at the end of the consultation, 'Thank you so much. You are the first doctor who has really listened to me.' 'Well – thank you for the encouragement.'

Of course I wondered to what extent it was true, and was she just flattering me? Certainly the fact she was able to stop her medication and in its place take just thyroxine tablets means she has become a very loyal patient.

The care of a patient over time is never perfect, so build that trust credit while the opportunity is there! Then when it becomes necessary to interrupt a consultation because of time constraints, or challenge a patient on a behavioural issue that is impacting their health, or apologise for a misunderstanding – you are more likely to be forgiven or to gain concordance. It is not a good idea to try to draw down on a trust account that is empty.

A PATIENT'S STORY

I saw a locum GP whom I had not met before and I was very upset afterwards. My mother had just died and I had come for a blood pressure review. He told me I was fat in no uncertain terms, and that unless I did something about it I would die young. I know I'm fat, but it wasn't the moment. I never want to see that locum again.

Indeed a long term robust relationship gives tremendous freedom to the clinician (and the patient) because of the trust that has built up. The doctor can try risking an intuitive leap, knowing that the patient will not take offence. For example: 'Tell me: do you think your headaches have anything to do with the bad relationship with your mother?'

When it comes to discussing worldview or seeking to offer spiritual comfort it is wise to have a relationship first. But it is not always possible.

A DOCTOR'S STORY

A 19 year old man was in the Intensive Therapy Unit on a ventilator after an accident. The parents sat beside him weeping, knowing that shortly the repeated tests would confirm death and that the ventilator would then be switched off. The anaesthetist found me downstairs. 'You're religious, aren't you?' 'No' I replied 'I'm not, but I do believe in the living God'. 'Whatever', he said, 'could you go to the ITU and offer some sort of comfort to those parents, the situation is awful.'

I approached the parents and put a hand on their shoulders from behind as they sat huddled together. 'I can't enter into what you are going through, but can I just offer you my deepest sympathy and our prayers that God will comfort you.' The man jumped up and grabbed me by the lapels of my white coat. He shook me violently. 'Don't you ever mention that word, God, to me again! What does he know about losing a son?' I looked at him and suddenly he realised what he had said. 'Oh, I'm sorry.'

'Don't apologise!' I replied. 'I have two sons and I can hardly imagine what it is to lose one, but indeed God gave his only Son, so he does know.' I pointed to the Gideon New Testament on the bed locker: 'I think you might find comfort in there'.

Sometimes we are thrust into situations where we are utterly out of our depth. The most important thing is to be there. Everything else is secondary. There is little time to think, let alone build trust or enjoy the luxury of taking a history of worldview. Touch can go wrong, speaking anything may backfire. Often we should just be present and mute. But if actions and words seem right we have to take the risk. Yes, of course we'll blow it, but God is able to use even our blundering and he and the patients tend to forgive our clumsy attempts to give comfort.

I remember seeing a 70 year old lady for the first time after her husband had died. I thought I knew her quite well and gave her a hug. It was definitely the wrong thing to do, judging by her frozen response! Usually I seemed to judge the touch, the hug, or the handshake OK, but not on that occasion!

Most patients are easily able to tell the difference between a genuine attempt at comfort and support and some crass proselytising. In fact you don't usually find people prone to the latter in the caring professions. Perhaps it would be unwise of me to suggest which professions they do choose! Gentleness, sensitivity and permission are a good guard against offensive behaviour.

On the occasion when God does ambush us with a surprise (which incidentally often teaches us more of ourselves and him than the routine of our days, according to Henri Nouwen [78]) then we have to have faith that we are already equipped with the experience and wisdom, perhaps send an 'arrow' prayer, and do the best we can.

A GP'S STORY

A married Asian lady I knew quite well attended with low back pain and after assessment I offered to pray for her back. She accepted gladly and when she returned for review it had settled and she was fully mobile. But on this occasion, instead of looking pleased she burst into floods of tears. It turned out she was infertile and her mother had left her on a visit back to Pakistan and had said on departure: 'You had better be pregnant when I return, or else!'
So on this visit she asked me to pray for her infertility which I did.

She conceived but at seven months of pregnancy she called me because she had suddenly become aware that there were no foetal movements. When I examined her I could feel no movements and using the fetal stethoscope could not hear a heartbeat (there was no portable Doppler available). I felt desolate. 'Everything is alright isn't it, doctor?' I had the sudden thought that either God is there, or he isn't, and that it was entirely right to say, 'It's fine, and to be sure I'm sending you for a scan at the hospital'. She later phoned happily to let me know the baby was well and she then went on to a normal delivery.

This story raises a number of issues, so do consider carefully how you would have answered the question and why. It is perhaps worth a reminder at this point of what I said in the Preface, that I don't necessarily agree with what was said or done in the stories I have presented. On reflection there is often a better way that a given situation could have been handled.

Sometimes we know in advance that things are going to be particularly difficult.

A GP'S STORY

I approached the cottage through its beautiful garden in some trepidation. I knew I was going to be grilled by an angry grieving family. Thankfully I knew God wanted me there. Only the previous evening the sermon had been from the book of Revelation and warned that God knew about impending difficulties: 'Do not be afraid of what you are about to suffer'. Hopefully it didn't include some of the events promised in subsequent verses – imprisonment and death!

The sermon had been a helpful reminder that God knew all about suffering for trying to do good. After the sermon a friend had objected to the tone of some parts of it: 'He made us out to be victims – we don't need to have a victim mentality'. And I agreed. My friend's objection reminded me that I had a clear conscience over the matter in question and I was free to love and try to support the family after a mysterious death. So here I was walking from my car to the cottage well prepared, warned that a trial was ahead, and determined not to be defensive. But, well, I was still apprehensive!

Initially it was worse than I expected. My entry into the crowded sitting room was met with scowls on most faces. I was ushered into the remaining empty armchair. 'If I was a younger man I'd strangle you with my bare hands' said a man I had never met before. Being a fairly slow thinker, I'm never quick to give an answer but that one made me pause longer than usual.

'I haven't met you all before' I said. 'Could we do a round of introductions?' We proceeded and I was introduced to some of the many relatives of the deceased, George. In his early 80s, George had been the lynch pin of this complicated family over many years. He was known to me as the quiet centre, loved by all. I had promptly diagnosed his bowel cancer two years previously and thus enabled him to have a quick and apparently curative operation. A few weeks before his death, however, he had presented with abdominal pain and a palpable mass in the abdomen. I suspected a recurrence. He was referred back to hospital. Before the review happened the family requested a home visit as George was depressed.

A colleague visited and started some antidepressants. But two days later George felt worse and said he just wanted to die. The mass in the abdomen was tender and after discussion he was readmitted to hospital where he suddenly collapsed and died that night. Death was thought to have been from an overwhelming infection and not the cancer. The family had been furious. Why had the infection not been diagnosed? Why had hospital admission been delayed by two days? There were many questions.

I had agreed to meet the family. First I said how sorry I was about George's death. We proceeded through what had happened and then the family asked numerous questions, many very insightful. Some clearly felt guilty they hadn't taken George's illness seriously enough. We made a list of questions for me to ask the hospital.

I assured them of what I knew of their love for George and how willingly he would have forgiven them for anything they felt they'd done wrong. I then apologised if by tone or assumption we had prevented George getting curative treatment in time. I appealed to them that we had all wanted to do the best we could. As I spoke to them the miracle for me personally was that in my heart I simply cared for these people in their grief without fear, resentment, or concerns about my reputation.

The hospital responded very carefully and thoughtfully to all the issues we raised. The grief of this situation for me was actually something different. There appeared to be no faith in a good God to support the family at such a time. Death really is a disaster if there is nothing beyond. Guilt and anger mixed powerfully in the complex relationships of a big family. But the fact was that over many years members of the family had come to trust our clinic, and in this crisis the relationship weathered the storm.

There must be trust both ways in the professional relationship. Sometimes when I have suggested a chaperone, the patient has been highly offended, seeing it as a sign that I don't trust them. And anyway, who is this chaperone that they should trust them? If trust is not present, consultations will be long and arduous to make sure every 'i' is dotted and every 't' crossed.

'What is required of us is that we exhibit Christ-like character, competence in our profession, compassion, communication that is wise, and courage' (Bob Snyder). [79] When patients trust you deeply they will go out of their way to get your opinion.

A GP'S STORY

A male patient with recurrent paranoid schizophrenia was detained in the locked ward of the local mental hospital during a relapse of his illness. I was rather surprised to see him at an appointment in my community clinic some five miles from the hospital! He had made the appointment himself and then made his escape and circumvented the hospital's security system.

He wanted my advice as to whether his memory was real or playing tricks with him. He recounted in vivid detail a violent episode from his childhood involving a gun. He found recounting the story unpleasant and then asked me: 'Do you think this actually happened?' As I was in possession of his lifelong medical record I was able to show him the notes and letters. There was no mention of any such problem, court case, or the psychological assessments that would have accompanied such a tragedy. I said I was convinced from his case record that no such thing had happened and that his abnormal brain chemistry was giving him these false memories.

Remarkably, he was satisfied with my explanation and took himself back to the hospital. I suppose we had known each other a long time and even through the confusion of his horrible hallucinations and delusions he felt he could trust me. As you might expect I did then phone the hospital team, advise them of the encounter, and suggest that a tightening of their security was warranted!

Even with the best motivation in the world we will make mistakes as clinicians. We certainly need to put in place systems which keep patients, our colleagues, and ourselves as safe as possible. This safety needs to be balanced by practicality. At present I have to negotiate six locks and four passwords when I arrive at work in the morning, before I have done anything!

My experience is that patients who trust their doctor, and are confident that the doctor means well, are very forgiving on those occasions when a mistake is made.

A GP'S STORY

I attended a patient at home with severe low back pain. After having given an injection for pain relief I returned to the clinic. When I checked the batch number on the ampoule for the case notes, I discovered I had given him the wrong drug – a diuretic. In a rather agitated state I told one of my colleagues. I was given a hug and my colleague committed the situation to God with a prayer. I phoned the patient, explained the error, and apologised before advising of the importance of supplementing with oral fluids.

'That's OK, doc, don't worry about it' he said. 'But there is one thing: could you call back and give me the injection of the painkiller?' Which I gladly did. And nowadays I always read the ampoule ingredients and expiry date out loud to the patient and to myself.

A GP REGISTRAR'S STORY

My patient gently explained to me that usually Muslim men don't shake hands with women and not to be offended that he didn't shake my proffered hand.

This story reminded me of the importance of not handing something to people from south east Asia with your left hand. Because of the uses to which the left hand is put, it is considered unclean, and handing something with it is thus usually a deliberate insult. I still recoil slightly myself if someone hands me something with their left hand and I only worked there for a few years. Being willing to learn the do's and don'ts of different cultures builds trust and can be fun too.

Sometimes it is in hard situations that trust emerges rapidly – when you are the patient's last hope.

A GP'S STORY

A 52 year old office worker attended in desperation. His boss had told him to come because he could no longer cope with work, and

*threatened him with suspension otherwise. He had developed a severe
alcohol problem over the preceding year. He had cut himself off from
his son and friends, and living alone, had ceased to take care of his
bills. He was in severe arrears with his mortgage after a divorce and
he was about to lose his flat and the deposit he'd put into it.*

*He was suicidal, shaky, sleepless, malnourished and, of course, he
stank of alcohol. He wanted help. Actually he really wanted help.
Towards the end of the assessment I asked if he had a faith in God.
He said he had, but was not part of any faith community. I said that
I thought this crisis had come because God wanted to show him
something good and that good could come out of it. Together we
worked out a plan for detoxification from the alcohol and regular
support while he came off it.*

*The surprising thing to me was that I barely knew him but he trusted
me completely about the plan. We discussed the medication and
withdrawal symptoms and I gave him sickness certification for work
and suggested the local specialist agencies that support alcoholics,
including AA.* [80] *I also suggested that his son might be interested
in taking a share in his flat and might be only too glad to have
a relationship back with a sober Dad. We planned out how he
might approach his son.*

*Remarkably he went through it all and was reconciled with his
son who did indeed take a share in the flat. He contacted friends
he hadn't spoken to for a long time to ask for help with his
detoxification, and they came up trumps and agreed to spend
time with him. I saw him regularly over several months and the
transformation was amazing. His gratitude and happiness was
overflowing – it seemed to me mainly because he had discovered
that he was loved. He was alive again.*

Trust accounts also need to be built up with colleagues. It is very
worthwhile investing time in building relationships with colleagues –
after all, isn't life mainly about relationships? After many courteous
exchanges with the local pharmacy, which included 'n' prescriptions, [81]
a friendly pharmacist phoned me on one occasion.

'You didn't really mean to issue this patient with a prescription for Mickey Mouse, did you, Dr McAll?' On our clinical computer system's learning module we had a family of patients to practise our computer skills on, and the family consisted of some well known cartoon characters, including Mickey, Minnie and Donald. In my haste to sort out a prescription for someone, I had forgotten to exit the training module!

There have been many occasions in my career when a colleague has rescued patient care by watching my back, or who has forgiven me for some idiocy. People will have a natural inclination not to watch your back if they dislike you and don't trust you; it is not only you, but the patients who will suffer. And as we'll see in Chapter 10, trust can bring great freedom in conversation with colleagues.

8. THE CLINICIAN'S FAITH REVEALED

'You are the salt of the earth...You are the light of the world.' [82]

'God calls us to be salt (being a touch from God) and light (showing a glimpse of God) in our medical workplaces. God is already at work in the lives of your patients – God's workplace – so your goal is to show them the way to faith at the pace God sets for them, always with permission, sensitivity, and respect. To bring out the faith of your patients and share your own, you will need to pray continually, that is, cultivate a constant awareness of God being with you throughout the day.' [83]

'The willingness to be forgiven is our main testimony.' [84]

When should clinicians speak of their own faith? First of all there are the times when we are obliged to explain our own worldview when we are unable, for reasons of our belief, to follow a course of action which the patient is requesting.

In its guidance for doctors the General Medical Council (GMC) in the UK states that there is an obligation to explain our worldview to a patient if we are unable to give advice or carry out a procedure because of our beliefs. So under certain circumstances patients are given a right to know their clinician's worldview.

The GMC also expects us to explain the patient's right to see another doctor in this situation: 'If carrying out a particular procedure or giving advice about it conflicts with your religious or moral beliefs, and this conflict might affect the treatment or advice you provide, you must explain this to the patient and tell them they have the right to see another doctor. You must be satisfied that the patient has sufficient information to enable them to exercise that right. If it is not practical for a patient to arrange to see another doctor, you must ensure that arrangements are made for another suitably qualified colleague to take over your role.' [85]

Note that if the doctor advises a course of action that is in the best medical interest of a patient then he or she is under no obligation to explain the worldview. It is only where there might be a conflict between the carrying out of a procedure, or the giving of advice, and the doctor's beliefs that the doctor must explain his or her position.

But what does the GMC have to say when it comes to other occasions? 'You must treat your patients with respect whatever their life choices and beliefs. You must not unfairly discriminate against them by allowing your personal views to affect adversely your professional relationship with them or the treatment you provide or arrange. You must not express to your patients your personal beliefs, including political, religious or moral beliefs, in ways that exploit their vulnerability or that are likely to cause them distress.' [86]

Christians should have little difficulty with this and the helpful additional notes. There is no attempt to muzzle freedom of speech and conscience. But I hope I have at least caused discomfort, if not distress, by challenging racist views expressed by patients, and on one occasion challenging a patient who felt it their right to murder a social worker (and in the latter case, warning the police).

WHY SPEAK ABOUT OUR OWN FAITH?

There are several reasons why we might speak of our own faith with patients. First, because we are convinced that commitment to a religious faith improves the health of patients. Secondly, as Christians, we will long for the patient to recognise that God is in the consulting room too and that he understands suffering and wants to bless.

Communication in this situation requires gentleness, permission and respect – our model in this regard is a far higher standard than the strictures of the medical or nursing councils, it is the standard of Christ himself who always perfectly addressed the needs of the person with whom he was dealing even in the most difficult circumstances. [87] His help was not conditional on their acceptance of him, though a lack of gratitude to God clearly deeply disturbed him. [88] He was consistently gentle with those who were suffering. He tailored his help to the exact need of the individual. He encouraged his followers to go to those who were ready to receive them, and not to push on closed doors. [89]

The issue that must not be forgotten is the status difference, the power imbalance. Doctor and patient are equal in the eyes of God. But the medic, as a professional, usually has more knowledge (or at least different knowledge) about diseases than the patient, and is in a position of power to assist. The patient is often vulnerable, confused and distracted. They may be acutely aware of the status difference, especially if the doctor uses technical language. Jesus never used his power to manipulate others, but had a deep respect for individual autonomy even when he could see it was leading to disaster.

He also resisted being manipulated. It is the doctor's duty to do what is needed (rather than what is wanted, which is sometimes very different) with empathy [90] and gentleness. The patient's wellbeing and that of the community are the prime concerns in the consultation, and we should not speak of other matters to satisfy our own needs. If we treat every patient as we would treat royalty, we may not go far wrong (but that might depend on your view of monarchy).

Harold Koenig is a keen advocate of spiritual history and has investigated carefully the beneficial effects on health outcomes of religious observance, but he is rather more guarded when it comes to clinicians offering spiritual counsel. In his wide ranging review *Medicine, Religion and Health* he states: [91] 'I believe the overall goal of the clinician is to find common ground with all patients, and that means not trying to change beliefs, but rather trying to support beliefs that help patients cope'.

I think the clinician's goal is actually slightly different from this – it is to make a correct and truthful diagnosis and discern the best treatment options for the patient to choose from. The patient has a right to the truth, and will have insights into the truth about their own physical, psychological, social and spiritual state that we don't have. We should develop insights into the truth of their situation and together we can explore areas of doubt. The point is that clinician and patient together are truth seekers, and beliefs may need to change in any of those areas for treatment and healing to proceed. We don't need to collude with lies, although we must be cautiously respectful and aware of our own fallibility. We seek to help the patient to face the truth and what needs to be done. The patient, as with any proffered opinion or treatment, has the right to reject it, and should never be abandoned when they do. This is in the context of 'cure sometimes, treat often, comfort always',[92] because so often what is to be done is not clear, and there is mystery.

If patients don't wish to know the truth about some aspect of the diagnosis, they usually make this clear.

A DOCTOR'S STORY

A patient had a diagnosis of lung cancer. I asked, 'So, have you had the opportunity to ask all the questions you want to about your illness? Is there anything you'd like to know?'

The patient replied 'Isn't it a lovely spring day? I'm so looking forward to spending some time in my greenhouse this afternoon when I get home.'

In a similar way patients will usually signal clearly when they don't wish faith issues to be explored. The clinician should not push at a closed door. The Christian clinician believes that God's work in people's lives is at different stages, so look for the prepared heart. On the other hand, to deny allowing a patient to consider a beneficial intervention because of political correctness would be negligent. So too would be the failure to challenge a harmful notion. Dr Koenig's view is that once a spiritual issue is uncovered, then onward referral to a chaplain is best. The problem with this is that the trusting relationship developed over a long time with a doctor is not instantly transferable. In a culture such as the

UK there is now much less of a tradition of seeking advice from faith leaders if one is not already part of a faith community.

It is rare that a clinician will be able to offer more than a brief intervention, but because of the particular situation these can be incisive and, on occasions, life changing. In an age of professionalism and subspecialty, many medical staff feel themselves to be 'amateurs' in this area and so feel unqualified to speak. Or perhaps, as Daniel Sulmasy suggests,[93] there is a discomfort with the idea of crossing the boundary between the roles of pastor/priest and medical professional. He argues that these roles should be separate but mutually supportive and enhancing.

If we 'prescribe faith' for its biomedical health benefits there is the obvious problem that this could reduce faith (and God) to a useful means to an end, equivalent to prophylactic aspirin. Anthropocentrism,[94] man-centred thinking, is at the heart of the Christian diagnosis of what is wrong with mankind. But we all come to God with very mixed motives and if the evidence suggests that religious commitment enhances physical health then patients have a right to know this. If that stimulates enquiry, the patient may find more than they sought, as most Christians coming to Christ with a great jumble of motives have found.

AN ONCOLOGIST'S STORY

I have always found the hospital consultant setting difficult, as we are almost never on our own with patients. Because of this, I took a conscious decision to concentrate on going round the hospital on one Sunday a month in my white coat and inviting all the patients to a service which I ran in the hospital chapel. This was very well attended at first but over 18 years the numbers steadily dwindled to almost nothing. This was a powerful barometer for me of how our society saw the established church become more and more irrelevant over that period, and after much soul searching I gave up this activity.

I too recall this activity as a medical student with a team of healthcare workers and students running services in the old Lambeth Hospital and at St Thomas' Hospital. In many hospitals around the UK and the world chaplaincy teams, supported by healthcare workers, run a variety of activities for patients, and the simple involvement of people from all disciplines demonstrates to patients that it is quite acceptable to express their faith while in hospital.

In my own hospital practice, if I felt sometimes on a ward round there were issues that needed to be explored privately with a patient, I would make time and come back after the ward round, or delegate the task to another. One to one times need to be protected in the hospital environment. These may be with the junior doctor, the nurse, the cleaner, the chaplain – but it is vital that one member of the team gets one to one time with a patient to allow the patient to express some of their deepest concerns, which will often include faith issues.

Indeed it is often the cleaners, who are so unthreatening, who hear the greatest intimacies and get the real story. They are ignored by the other 'professionals' much of the time and so their contribution to understanding what the patient really feels may well be missed. In the short and long term these conversations can make a big difference to the patient's wellbeing and so it is possible an over-zealous management culture that concentrates on hard targets and chaperones will backfire into reduced patient satisfaction, slower recoveries and possibly increased litigation.

Some clinicians have told me that because they are rarely alone with patients, both patient and healthcare worker are inhibited about speaking of very personal issues such as faith. Not all healthcare workers are inhibited by the presence of the crowd and they can model a willingness to break taboos.

A SURGEON'S STORY

Mr B had gastric cancer and I had performed a total gastrectomy. On a post-operative ward round I arrived at the bed with the usual entourage to find him reading the Gideons New Testament.[95] *'Are you enjoying what you're reading?' I asked. 'Yes, it's a good book' he replied.*

'I think that will do far more good for you than my operation' I said. At that he looked rather worried! He thought I had bad news about the operation. 'What do you mean?'

'Let me put it this way: The operation went really well and I hope the operation I've done will reduce your suffering and do you good in this life, but that book will teach you the truth about eternal life. But now then – how are you today?'

Just after that he went home. The ward sister phoned me anxiously: 'Mr B has stolen the New Testament!' 'Oh, we don't need to worry about that' I replied. Mr B died 18 months later and his wife wrote me a letter after the funeral. 'He loved that book, and he died clutching it to his chest. It meant so much to him. I'd like to keep it if that's OK.'

This story interests me because the doctor was in the presence of other staff. This was not something hidden and he wasn't embarrassed just to be himself, seeking a link with the patient. No one would give it a second thought if the patient had been reading the sports pages of the newspaper or an advert for a computer, and the consultant had asked about Spurs or megabytes.

To try to censor the conversation of hospital workers would demonstrate a lack of trust and an attack on free speech. As the quid pro quo, workers who enjoy this freedom of speech will reasonably be expected to get the work done, giving extra time if necessary.

Patients can become very interested in knowing about their healthcare team. Part of the development of a trusting relationship does involve a certain degree of the sharing of self by the health staff. The key here is that the patient wants to know something of your story, so develop the art of brief story telling. Amongst the general chit chat about life, worldview doesn't need to be kept secret! 'Faith stories go a little further by explaining how God, prayer, or a biblical principle became relevant to you or someone else.'[96] This enables the patient not only to trust the doctor (hopefully!) but also builds the sense of being part of community.

A GP'S STORY

A Chinese lady came to see me in the clinic. She was studying Chinese history in our city. It turned out she was from a city in China where my parents had previously worked as doctors in a medical school. She was very interested, as her period of study coincided with the time my parents were there. I was able to give her a copy of their biography with a proviso about some of its Christian content.

I have an interest in environmental issues and patients like to pick up on that, often making some playfully rude comments about my electric car [97] to which I reply, 'Ah – but I'm saving the earth!' One patient even says 'And how is my car doing?' (as if it is his). Another said 'I'm flying off to Canada on holiday and I suppose you think I should carbon mitigate my flight?' 'Good idea' I replied. 'Look at Climate Stewards online.' [98]

One doctor I met had a credit card sized biography printed on the back of his calling card, which patients can have if they wish to. This tells something of the story of how he came to be where he is now and what his faith means to him. He cleared the content with the GMC as he had no desire to proselytise or offend patients.

While friends often become patients, it is more unusual for patients to become close friends. But sometimes sharing our lives with patients can lead to surprising consequences.

AN ONCOLOGIST'S STORY

I was seeing a lady with cancer and praying for both her and her husband. I had found that because I was seeing them privately I had a bit more time with them undisturbed. The husband asked me to do a sponsored cycle ride with him. That ride was the start of a cycling group, and the men who did the long rides wanted to know more about the Bible.

As a consequence a Bible study group formed and we have done many other things together as a group. Through that one patient contact and his friends and family, my wife and I have become part of the life of a number of non-believer families, and they have become part of ours.

9. SHORTCUTS

When time is tight, we all long for a shortcut to an answer in consultations. We try to become agile in developing a rounded understanding of a patient's problems. Sometimes it is clear that the patient's agenda is really extremely simple. On one occasion a middle aged man entered my consulting room and placed a small piece of paper on my desk.

'Could you read this for me, Doc?' I read: 'Bohemian Dawn, 4:15, Haydock'. He thanked me very warmly and left. This brief incident revealed a great deal about my patient. Where can you go in complete confidence in the UK, when you live alone and are illiterate, to get a free reminder of which horse you had put a bet on, without embarrassing yourself in front of your friends? His idea to see me was an ingenious solution! By the way, I can confirm that the race is long since over so this is no longer a hot tip! Except to show how much you can learn about someone in 20 seconds.

Usually things are more complicated! Understanding in depth the background of the patient's life may be critical at arriving at an understanding of the presenting problem. We want to reach these issues of the moment and then seek a way forward. But so often we fail to find, let alone address, the key points. We often have to close down discussion of the ever broadening complexities of a patient's life to bring back the focus. Instead we use the interventions at our disposal, such as the prescription pad, as a quick but often superficial solution.

As a Christian with faith that God has actually planned this encounter, it would be great to know what God thinks. Perhaps this arises from my inherent laziness; I want the perfect 'quick fix' so I can get on! Another reason is that we all desire the natural security of the simple answer; it keeps our worldview simple. We want the simplicity of cure instead of the hard work of care. We want to solve everything now. This desire for the right answer can be passionately intense as we sit, in ignorance and powerlessness, alongside the sufferer. Usually knowledge will have to come through the gifts we have been given already, the skilful application of careful watching and listening (and sometimes sniffing!), the answers to well-chosen questions, and then examination and investigations. The problems can then be summarised or formulated into classical categories (eg physical, psychological, social or worldview) and addressed.

But then sometimes, just sometimes, something different seems to happen. Jesus tailored his healing interventions to the exact need of the person before him. Often the interactions were extraordinarily brief and concise. Clearly this is partly the natural abbreviation of the storytellers, but in the cut and thrust of his often hectic life it is absolutely clear that Jesus was, at the very least, a very quick thinker. He also spent a lot of time alone in prayer, thinking things through, so he was well prepared. In Luke's gospel we even have his words and actions recorded by a thoughtful physician. Jesus tailors his words and actions to the precise needs of the sufferer on all levels. As we read the stories they also speak to us in our particular needs at different times. Could we manage to do something like this with our own patients in the 21st century?

THE SUDDEN INSIGHT

In his enjoyable book *Blink*,[99] Malcolm Gladwell describes how anyone can have sudden impressions about a new situation that bypass their cognitive functions, because of expertise, experience or preconceptions. Sometimes these impressions are correct, sometimes dangerously wrong. As cognitive processes can sometimes be slow, there can be important survival benefits of these instant impressions. Gladwell uses varying examples from the amusing (expert assessment of fake antiques) to the deadly serious (preconditioning of police that dangerously affects their judgments when attending an emergency call).

The same sort of thing can occur in a medical consultation and is perhaps best referred to as an 'intuitive leap'. The outcome or thought following an intuitive leap may be offered to the patient for consideration. The Christian is looking for an intuitive leap, based on the wealth of experience and understanding, and hopes to be aided by the Holy Spirit. These usually come unbidden and seem to me to be rare, but can easily be ignored if not listened for. One way to attempt to find missed prompts or intuitive leaps in a consultation is to review a videoed consultation, press the 'stop' button, and ask the clinician 'What was in your mind at this point?'

A GP'S STORY

I called the name of my next patient and then stood waiting for her to join me to be led to the consulting room. She was about 27 years old and was new to the surgery. As she walked towards me something inside me said 'She suffered sexual abuse as a child'. She sat down and it turned out that she had severe tonsillitis which we dealt with.

Then I plucked up courage and said, 'Have you ever had the opportunity to properly address the hurts from your past?' She seemed at once to relax as if I knew all about it, which felt somewhat strange. She told me that the previous year she had had a course of psychotherapy, but the money had run out just as she was beginning to deal with the main issue. I told her I thought we could help and gave her the details of an excellent free local service for counselling women who had suffered abuse, which she gladly accepted. It was a brief consultation.

As she left I was still surprised at what had happened. On reflection I wondered if it was the way she dressed or her hairdo that reminded me of other patients. Or, awesome thought, had the Holy Spirit prompted me?

If you have accepted what was discussed in Chapter 5 about dualism, I hope you might agree that the answer to both these questions is yes, probably. Notice that there had been little time in the consultation to develop trust, so the GP was understandably cautious in offering the question.

A GP's STORY

I looked at the appointment list on the computer and saw the name of the 21 year old patient who was next. I was immediately sure that this lady had been raped. It was received as a sudden thought impression, not as an audible voice. I'm usually very cheerful and breezy when I go into the waiting room to invite patients through, but, in view of the thought I'd had, I decided to approach the patient more seriously and gently.

The young lady looked tidy, was well made up and appeared emotionally stable. There were no obvious signs of distress. The problem she wished to discuss was minor. Once this minor issue had been dealt with, I said, 'I think you are very distressed about something: do you want to talk about it?' The patient did indeed want to talk about it, and had recently been raped. We were able to address the issues together.

These flashes of insight need to be handled with care in the intense atmosphere of the consultation, and offered with due caution. It would be rare to be more than provisional. A more definite concluding statement can be reserved for a summary once the discussion has reached agreement.

A GP's STORY [100]

Starting the car to go home one evening, the thought came into my mind that I should visit a family I had not seen for some time. I resisted the idea, firstly because I was tired and secondly because the family had not asked for a visit and it might be difficult to explain why I had gone. It could be just one of these bright ideas which led nowhere. I therefore took the common-sense way and turned the car homeward. But the thought quietly persisted. I did a U-turn and headed for the family's home. I had heard it said that it is better to make a mistake than make nothing.

> *When I knocked on the door, it was opened by the wife who,*
> *without a word of welcome or even surprise, withdrew hastily into*
> *the kitchen on the left. Father then appeared briefly in the doorway*
> *of the sitting room on the right. The eight year old daughter sat*
> *with her chin on her hands, half-way up the staircase in the middle,*
> *and looked at me with large unhappy eyes.*
>
> *I closed the door behind me and stepping into the small hall, waited*
> *for someone to say something. At last mother said, 'We've come to*
> *the end of the road. Either he goes or I go.' I stood silently praying*
> *for some illuminating thought, but as none came, I said 'Well, I*
> *don't know what the answer is, but I do know that God minds what*
> *happens to you all, because he told me to come. I am sure he can*
> *tell you what to do.' There was no comment from either room so,*
> *after a few more moments of complete silence, I let myself out of the*
> *house and went home.*
>
> *I heard nothing more, but a few weeks later I caught a glimpse of*
> *them in a crowded place. They all waved cheerfully and it was clear*
> *that all was well. I met the daughter recently and she confirmed that*
> *the family was still together and happy.*

God can, if he wishes, write a message for you on the wall. It is probably
better not to wish for that. The only person in the Bible who had such
a message was a king who was dead by the next day! The message was
'You have been weighed on the scales and found wanting'. [101] But rarely
and graciously, it would seem that he may suddenly give you some hint
or push towards the answer to the patient's immediate problem, if you
are aware that this might happen. Be on the lookout for these surprises,
for if we deny God the opportunity to communicate however he wants,
rather than how our theological system prescribes, we may find we have
confined God in a box in our thinking – God with a small 'g'.

The occasional flash of insight is no excuse for a lack of education and
careful preparation, or a substitute for experience. For most of the time
it is persevering, curious, empathetic servanthood that is required. As
Eugene Peterson has it: [102] 'In desperate times we are tempted to go for
the quick answer and the efficient solution. The quick answer is almost

always the oversimplified one, leaving out all the complexities of actual truth; the efficient solution is almost always the depersonalised one, for persons take a lot of time and endless trouble.' God is also in the long answers.

10. RAISING FAITH WITH COLLEAGUES

THE STORY OF ONE NURSE, TOLD BY A COLLEAGUE

It is extraordinary the impact one nurse can have on the atmosphere in a ward, even a junior nurse. On the neonatal unit where I worked there was an outstanding Christian nurse. She rarely spoke of her faith. But it was apparent in the way she treated the babies, the parents, and the staff in the unit. She had a respect for the weakest, didn't patronise people, and went out of her way to understand and respect each one's unique concerns.

One of her early initiatives was to introduce free visiting so that parents, relatives and siblings of patients could come on the ward at any time. This required overcoming resistance to change but her approach was always to stick calmly to the evidence of benefit and to persuade people. Relatives had always been forced to change into special clothes and ours was one of the earliest units in the country to accept that gowns were unnecessary and that hand washing was the key infection prevention strategy. She proved that special clothes were not needed and she would steadily strip away resistance to change with good evidence and yet was always ready to listen and change her own views.

Her big aim was to get parents involved in the care of their babies as much as possible, trying to make the unit feel like home from home. She encouraged the siblings to come and, realising that they got bored when the parents needed to spend a lot of time with the baby, organised an area where they could play so that the parents wouldn't be anxious. She patiently explained to the other nurses each change and induced a flexible approach. She welcomed all the uncles and aunts and grandparents.

Slowly the statistics and clinical outcomes demonstrated the wisdom of the innovations, and the unit found they were getting better results year on year. The unit became increasingly popular as people felt listened to.

I think that much of this was to do with giving away power and control. Often professionals feel comfortable when they are in control. Creating rules can be more about 'my space', 'my power' and 'my convenience' than the needs of the patient or client. Rules point to who is boss, so in giving away control and power we found that parents started to feel a sense of ownership. This nurse empowered the relatives to feel capable of making suggestions. They became more confident and had good ideas which were acted on. Naturally there were occasional abuses of the trust she put in people, which required a response. She especially seemed to go out of her way with those who were the most vulnerable and pathetic; for example the babies whose parents were less attentive.

When it came to Christmas she personally arranged a stocking for each baby with something unique and appropriate. As the years went by she steadily gained allies who then supported her next initiative. She said little about her faith, preferring to let others speak because she liked to focus on the immediate need and practical action. She was not interested in making a point or gaining kudos. She seemed to be able to put herself in the shoes of others, for example empathising with the single mother who was a refugee from a developing country, despite the fact she was single and had no children of her own.

It didn't feel like a ward, it just felt baby and parent friendly. In a neonatal intensive care unit with extremely premature babies there are, of course, sadly, deaths. It became apparent to her that parents found it difficult to feel the reality and importance of the short life of their baby who had lived only in the unit. When the parents went home the neighbours had never seen the baby. The baby had not been home and life just somehow went on.

To many parents in this situation there is a feeling of unreality as if the baby never existed, or was of no significance. So our nurse met with the allies she had made in the chaplaincy team (they had felt a welcome on the ward too). They considered what might be done for these grieving parents and decided that an act of remembrance together that recognised all the babies might be helpful. The service that evolved was clearly Christian and interdenominational, as inclusive as possible, respectful and open. The service made no assumptions about those attending and parents determined the structure and brought their own contributions of music, poems and prayers. The event worked really well. There was naturally a wide range of contributions from pieces of doggerel to the sophisticated quotations of the erudite. These were often in moving juxtaposition to each other – whatever parents and families had found significant.

This gathering gave the opportunity to celebrate the significance of these little lives and became very important to the parents who drew comfort from being with others who had been through similar times, and through being back with the staff who for a period had made them feel at home. Siblings attended too, and the event has become an annual pilgrimage for many, an important part of grieving and of remembering. It is helpful just to be reassured that somewhere in the world there are people who remember and understand. It is living theology. And actually the nurse's understanding was that the incarnation of Jesus Christ is key. At the heart of it all is that God became a baby and made himself fragile. The service has become more than an act of pity; it is one of respect and hope.

The colleague who told me this story added his own comment: 'It is so typical of the way God does things: He acts first and explains things later'. And this is true in so many areas: in that great textbook of life, the Bible, and in the life and teaching of Christ, in creation, and even in my own life. It is a promise from God for a future understanding. He acts first and explains things later. 'Now we see but a poor reflection as in a mirror; then we shall see face to face.' [103] The nurse in the above story was willing to make herself the servant of all.

There are aspects of the patient-clinician interaction which make them unique, but many of the prompts and restraints we have discussed are a useful guide to our interactions with colleagues and friends. These include the importance of a life of servanthood, the development of mutual trust, the use of faith flags, and common seeking for truth. These are all applicable to our relationships with colleagues. And as with patients, a shared faith with colleagues can be a great encouragement.

A GP'S STORY

I was to be admitted to our local hospital for an investigation. I was somewhat anxious as I stepped into the hospital lift. In the lift there was one of the senior surgeons with a number of his team.

'Hi, Adam! What are you doing here?' 'I'm being admitted for an oesophagoscopy under GA [104]' I replied. 'I'll be praying for you. God bless you!' he said.

I could have imagined him saying this if we were alone, but what surprised me was that he was exactly the same in front of his junior staff. Then the anaesthetist came for the pre-operative check and he prayed for me. Then another colleague from the community who was doing a clinic at the hospital that day dropped by and he also prayed for me. I was touched by the love and faith of these friends, and reassured of God's love for me through them.

Jesus said his followers are 'salt and light' [105] and this applies to their workplace whether they like it or not. They are to bring their whole natures and gifts to work in partnership with others (salt's role is preserving what is good and enhancing taste when spread out). Don't forget that too much salt in one body in the wrong place raises blood pressure! And light – to be willing to explain the illustrating life with illuminating truth. And they are to do both in such a way that the credit goes to God.

A LABORATORY MEDICINE DOCTOR'S STORY

I was working in a team of three, and my two colleagues had an intense conflict with each other. They each came to me privately and complained bitterly and at length about the other. Speaking to one of them I said, 'I think that forgiveness may be the way forward here'. He replied 'That's a very Christian perspective'.

There was no sudden reconciliation, but this colleague backed off from his entrenched position and the situation eased. Another person who worked in the department informed me that I had become known as 'the carbon rod between the two nuclear reactors'! Subsequently this colleague and I had further discussions about Christian faith and these continue.

The first and most striking thing about this story is what had happened before it began – it is clear that the Christian in this setting was already known as someone who was approachable, who would listen and whose confidence could be trusted. This demonstrates integrity: a life where worldview and behaviour are well integrated together.

A DOCTOR'S STORY

The senior professor in my department, an agnostic, shared with me some of the pain of the divorce he was going through. As he finished I said, 'Arthur, can I pray for you?' 'Yes – thank you.'

A GP TRAINER'S STORY

A former registrar emailed me that she was applying for a new job and asking me to wish her luck. In my reply I reminded her that as a Christian I didn't believe in luck, but that I'd pray for her and hoped she'd get the job. A few weeks later I had a happy reply to the effect that my prayers were answered, and thanks.

As with patient interactions, colleagues will usually understand that an offer of prayer is an expression of care and concern. In my experience Muslim colleagues are particularly touched by the offer of intercessory prayer. And all colleagues are perfectly able to make it clear that they don't wish to engage in God talk.

One friend was speaking to a colleague who'd recently been widowed and mentioned something of his faith. The response came back, 'But that's completely irrelevant, isn't it?' Imagine that happening to you. Would you back off and change the subject, or would you come back with another question? What would determine which course you would take? Being a fairly slow thinker, that sort of reaction would usually stall me and I'd say nothing for a bit. We should learn sensitivity around this while not being intimidated into stopping being ourselves. To some extent this parallels the sensitivity of colleagues who don't swear or gossip in our presence because they know we'd be offended.

A GP'S STORY

A very experienced nursing sister accompanied me as we entered Ivor's room in the nursing home. He was a sharp but bedbound 78 year old. He laid his hand on a Bible that sat on his bed table and grinned. 'I've started reading this again,' he said, 'dipping in and out – it's very interesting.'

'What a good idea, it's the best of books,' I replied. 'I prefer works of non-fiction myself' said the sister. We then proceeded to tackle the problem of his chest infection. As I was halfway out of the door at the end, having said goodbye, he called out to me.

'Doctor!' 'Yes, Ivor?' 'Do have a happy Easter!' 'Thanks, and you too.' One day, if the opportunity is given, I hope to explore with the sister what lay behind her remark.

A SURGEON'S STORY

It was a Friday. Being a Muslim area, Friday was a weekend and so Church meetings were held on a Friday too. For Muslims, believing that prayer is one of man's highest duties because only we among all of God's creation can pray, attending Friday midday prayers was especially important.

A patient was admitted to our hospital with generalised peritonitis which turned out to be from a perforated appendix. I operated with a trainee surgeon, Ismail. As we were changing out of our theatre scrubs afterwards in the male changing area, Ismail said 'I should

*have been at the mosque now, and you should have been at church –
do you think we'll be forgiven?' I replied 'Well, Ismail, where do you
think God wanted us to be at this moment?' He smiled thoughtfully.*

Good clinicians need to be curious and empathetic. Consequently,
discussing worldview with medical colleagues is often great fun while
being deeply serious. I well remember a medical couple who were our
guests one evening. As we all settled ourselves comfortably into
armchairs after a wonderful dinner one of them said with a twinkle in
his eye, 'Now, you are Christians, and we want to know: do you believe
we are going to hell?' This led to a profound discussion of the issues of
life after death, and what it might mean not to respond to God's loving
free offer of life with him forever.

DEVELOPING CURIOSITY

We all know that not satisfying an appetite immediately can make it
more intense, and give more delight at its satisfaction in the right place
and at the right time. So it is with curiosity. It is best if it is not always
indulged at once – this is part of the art of fishermen. Fishing involves
an investment of time, great patience, skill and remarkable optimism, as
any fisherman will tell you. Christians are called to be fishers of men.

The following story illustrates curiosity encouraged, as well as the rule
of three. It is striking how, in Middle Eastern culture to this day, the
tradition of three questions followed by three replies or statements is a
way of ensuring the truth, for example when greeting someone or asking
about their health. This is best known to Christians in the three denials
and three affirmations of Peter, but it is scattered throughout the Bible.

A HOSPITAL DOCTOR'S STORY
*I was working in a country with Islam as a major religion. I was sitting
with three of my colleagues one day and we were discussing how much
hospital doctors were paid in my country. It suddenly struck them that
I'd be earning a lot more back home. So why had I come to work here?
This, after all, was a place that they felt they would perhaps like to get
out of if they were given the opportunity of greater pay elsewhere.
Knowing of their desire to travel and see the world, I replied that I had*

*been keen to experience the richness of another culture and see
something of the world outside my own country.*

*They acknowledged that this was desirable, but said there must be
something more to make it worthwhile. So I replied that my country
had been a colonial power in this area previously and had come with
basically selfish motives to develop trade and to profit from it, and
that I wanted to show a different spirit and try to give back some
service. That was laudable they replied, but past mistakes of my
country weren't my fault – that would be as irrational as young
Germans feeling guilty for the crimes of the Second World War.
So they insisted there must be some other reason.*

*Now I was on my third reply and their interest was intense. This was no
casual enquiry and the previous answers, though true, were partial. So I
compared Christian discipleship with pilgrimage in Islam, and said that
Christian pilgrimage started immediately on becoming a Christian and
that as opportunity arose Jesus had asked his followers to share his love
across cultures. One of them grinned at me: 'That is why you came'.*

So it is worth considering how to tailor one's approach to each colleague
and their needs. Just as a medical diagnosis and treatment takes time,
we know that discussing faith with colleagues needs an individually
tailored approach.

A DENTIST'S STORY

*The staff in the clinic often discuss what we've been up to outside
work. We'd been on a marriage enrichment course and this
intrigued the nurses who wanted to know more. This led on to a
discussion about how I met my wife, and how we'd saved sex to
marriage, and why. They were intrigued as to how one could have
faith that it would be OK. This has led on to all sorts of questions
– what is christening children all about, and what do we think
about life after death?*

What are you passionate about? It will inevitably overflow into
discussion with colleagues. One of my passions is this beautiful and
amazing planet of stardust of which we are stewards and a part.

So I warmly support A Rocha (Christians in conservation). [106] I took
a sabbatical to examine the health consequences of climate change.
Many colleagues asked me all about it and why, as a Christian, it
was important to me. What a privilege to be able to speak of this
awesome creation and a first cause: the mind, the love and power that is
behind it. And what fun to be cobelligerents with others with various
worldviews who are like minded on this issue.

We entertained a professor of orthopaedics who was visiting from China
and had become interested in Christian faith through reading *A Pilgrim's
Progress*, [107] one of the earliest Christian books to be translated into
Mandarin. While we were having our meal he asked, 'Do you think
God can speak to you through dreams?' 'Yes' I replied, 'as he did to
Joseph in the Bible'. 'Do you mean Mary's husband?' 'No, actually I
wasn't thinking about Joseph in the New Testament – I was thinking
of Joseph in the Old Testament.' 'New Testament I know, but what
is Old Testament?'

So I took him into the sitting room and we opened the Bible at
Genesis Chapter 1. In the kitchen my son, Ben, sighed to my wife,
'Poor Professor Lee! Dad has taken him to the sitting room and is
starting at the beginning of Genesis!'

It was fascinating to see Genesis through the eyes of someone who had
never read it before. The insights gained had direct application to his
own work situation and career progression. Later he introduced me to
other doctors and we were able to study the Gospel of Mark together
– again the extraordinary rapidity with which they grasped an
understanding of the character of Jesus amazed me.

In our multicultural society, engaging with the worldview of colleagues is
a vital part of working together and understanding each other. It is also
great fun.

11. JESUS AT WORK

MARK 5:21-43

When Jesus had again crossed over by boat to the other side of the lake, a large crowd gathered around him while he was by the lake. Then one of the synagogue rulers, named Jairus, came there. Seeing Jesus, he fell at his feet and pleaded earnestly with him, "My little daughter is dying. Please come and put your hands on her so that she will be healed and live." So Jesus went with him.

A large crowd followed and pressed around him. And a woman was there who had been subject to bleeding for twelve years. She had suffered a great deal under the care of many doctors and had spent all she had, yet instead of getting better she grew worse. When she heard about Jesus, she came up behind him in the crowd and touched his cloak, because she thought, "If I just touch his clothes, I will be healed." Immediately her bleeding stopped and she felt in her body that she was freed from her suffering.

At once Jesus realized that power had gone out from him. He turned around in the crowd and asked, "Who touched my clothes?"

"You see the people crowding against you," his disciples answered, "and yet you can ask, 'Who touched me?'"

But Jesus kept looking around to see who had done it. Then the woman, knowing what had happened to her, came and fell at his feet and, trembling with fear, told him the whole truth. He said to her, "Daughter, your faith has healed you. Go in peace and be freed from your suffering."

While Jesus was still speaking, some men came from the house of Jairus, the synagogue ruler. "Your daughter is dead," they said. "Why bother the teacher any more?"

Ignoring what they said, Jesus told the synagogue ruler, "Don't be afraid; just believe."

He did not let anyone follow him except Peter, James and John the brother of James. When they came to the home of the synagogue ruler, Jesus saw a commotion, with people crying and wailing loudly. He went in and said to them, "Why all this commotion and wailing? The child is not dead but asleep." But they laughed at him.

After he put them all out, he took the child's father and mother and the disciples who were with him, and went in where the child was. He took her by the hand and said to her, "Talitha koum!" (which means, "Little girl, I say to you, get up!"). Immediately the girl stood up and walked around (she was twelve years old). At this they were completely astonished. He gave strict orders not to let anyone know about this, and told them to give her something to eat.

As you will immediately gather from the long quote above, this chapter is different from the others. We have looked at many ways healthcare workers have addressed the 'God' question, and now I want to look at the example of the master of the craft – Jesus. This story has so many parallels with our situation – the pressure of the crowd with many needs and expectations, the difficult cultural nuances, the hard clinical problems. But it also has differences: two astounding, complete and instant healings. It repays study – and I'm sure you will add your own additional insights to mine. I suggest you read the story above once again before proceeding, even if it is familiar to you.

The story of Jesus' healing of the woman with bleeding is set in the middle of an apparent race against time to save a little girl's life. Imagine the impatience of the crowd! This woman probably felt unwell: breathless and tired from anaemia due to chronic blood loss. To appreciate the risk this lady took in touching Jesus we have to have an understanding of the prevailing culture (and, of course, her worldview). At that time a woman wasn't allowed to approach a man, let alone touch his clothes. A woman would always ask a male relative to make the approach to another man (as indeed Jairus had just done publicly on behalf of his family). This woman's direct approach tells us that she had no one, no male family member who could represent her. If she had been bleeding she was probably unmarriageable and infertile, perhaps widowed or divorced. Anyway she was grievously alone.

And she had clearly at one stage been a wealthy lady who had spent all her money on doctors (a point which Dr Luke omitted in his telling of this story!) It seems that their attention had only made things worse. May our patients and the God who owns them forgive us for the times when we have made things worse for those who are suffering.

Furthermore we know that she had been bleeding for twelve years, perhaps the whole of the life of the little girl who now lay dying. This was in all probability a gynaecological bleed. This bleeding made her a social outcast, because bleeding made a woman ritually unclean. [109] Everything she touched or sat on became unclean; relatives would find it impossible to function in society if they stayed around her. She would be unable to attend the synagogue which was the centre of the community life. Being unable to go to the synagogue meant she was excluded from the place of prayer – so she was cut off from God. There is no doubt that Mark was correct when he said that, even by the standards of those hard times, she had 'suffered a great deal'.

Now she planned to touch a man. That was bad enough, but to touch another man when you are unclean would contaminate him – you could be stoned simply for that. And consider this case: she has heard that Jesus is a very good man and an amazing healer – if she makes *him* unclean and ineffective what an enormous crime would that be? But she figures no one need know. She plans her timing with great care, covering her head (and face?) so as not to be known in the crowd or found out, terrified that she might be.

I wonder if you have ever been in a crowd that is rushing. I have, and it is an intimidating experience. Her moment comes in the hustle and bustle: she rushes and pushes and jostles and at last manages to touch Jesus' robe. She somehow knows at once that she is healed – what joy! But then...

Whoaa!! Jesus stops. To the utter mystification and confusion of his disciples, and doubtless the quiet desperation of Jairus, he will not budge until the one who touched is revealed. Like a schoolteacher suspending playtime, Jesus will not move until the culprit owns up. Jesus knows that something has happened, that he has been touched, that a physical healing has occurred. But he knows more – he understands that this was a healing sought in secret and that something more is needed.

For the woman, escape through the now stationary crowd is impossible. Found out, terrified and trembling she approaches Jesus, her face still concealed. She has interrupted the great man on his way to heal a little girl and indeed it appears she will be to blame for the death by causing the delay. She comes forwards and falls at his feet, and surely for her, judgment is about to fall and this is her last moment of life.

Then she hears one word: 'Daughter'. She can't believe her ears. Suddenly she discovers that she has been reconnected with a new Dad and through him a whole new family. I wonder at what point the veil was lifted from her face? She must have rocked with amazement as she hears that it is her faith that has healed her. What an encouragement! She has trusted Jesus in her moment of utter desperation and found him not only powerful, but good. She is commanded to go in peace and be freed from her suffering. The years of physical suffering, of psychological anguish, of disconnection from God, and of social exclusion are over. She enters a new life, free of disgrace and with new and restored relationships. And Jesus does it all with just two sentences. The law prescribes a sacrifice to make atonement after recovery from haemorrhage, but interestingly Jesus doesn't remind her of this.

The story then moves on to the little girl. The delay appears to have been fatal. But the girl is recalled to life. The irony is not lost on Mark – the attempt at a secret healing results in a public restoration, while the public request for healing brought a private resurrection. Two women, an old one who has bled for years and whose bleeding is arrested and life rescued, and a young one who is brought back to life and the menarché. Jesus was not satisfied with delivering physical healing by itself. Jesus' concern was for the whole person in community, and he had a clear grasp of the worldview and cultural implications of the situations in which he worked. He also had the compassion and power to restore life itself.

12. IS IT POSSIBLE TO BE LIKE JESUS?

A GP'S STORY

I had known him as a patient for about six years before Saleem told me of his background. His stepmother had put him on the streets at the age of five and after weeks living rough a kindly old gentleman had taken him in. Later this man abused Saleem. When he could escape he did, found work, and married in his teens.

But then his real mother contacted him pleading for money. He was touched by a longing to help her and to know the affection of the mother he had never had. He felt honour-bound to provide for her. He sold his house to send her the money she needed, only later discovering that she drank the money away: she was an alcoholic.

He had rows with his wife which led to domestic violence and divorce. He lost his job. He now felt guilty, useless, a failure in every sense, depressed. Having told me his tale Saleem stood in the consulting room and wept. I stood and hugged him while he shook with sobs. Gradually they subsided. Once he had checked his face in the mirror and cleaned up with the proffered tissue, taken his prescription for antidepressants, he said simply but with intensity, 'Thank you'. 'No, it is for me to thank you: you who have honoured me with these confidences' said I.

I asked a chaplain if it was possible to be like Jesus with patients?

A HOSPICE CHAPLAIN'S STORY

Oh I do it all the time. There was a family that was bitterly divided and the mother died. Planning the funeral with the undertaker was a matter of arduous shuttle diplomacy, and on one occasion I had to call the police when a fight between the factions broke out in the car park.

An example that illustrates how complicated it all was is that shortly after the funeral there was a phone call from a member of the family. 'You remember that it was agreed that her necklace would be divided equally?' 'Yes, that is written in the notes I took.' 'Was it agreed who was to pay for it to be divided up?' 'No, that wasn't discussed.'

Being involved in messy situations like this is the core of 'being Jesus'. First, it is actually to be present with that person (or people) in the place of suffering. Jesus existed with God the Father from eternity, and chose to humble himself from the position of ultimate power, authority and love to be restricted into the small space of a person, at a particular point in space and time. So our being present at a particular place and point in time with someone who needs us is already an imitation of Christ. 'The Christian clinician has the opportunity to communicate to the patient, even if more often implicitly that explicitly, an understanding of the bond that unites the suffering of all persons and redeems that suffering from abject lonely despair.' [110]

Secondly, even if we do weep on occasions, we bring a new dimension: hope for the future. 'Let not your hearts be troubled' [111] Jesus told his followers even as he faced the agony of death on a cross. He could say this because he knew what the future held.

We may have some useful professional tools to relieve suffering now, and wisdom to guide us, and these are such a gift; but we know in the core of our being that a relationship with God is the key link into the best life now, and the only solid basis for a future without suffering.

JOHN MARSH

One of my heroes is John Marsh, [112] a surgeon who, along with the other good surgeons there, took trouble to train me in Warwick. When he himself had been a junior doctor, he had been embarrassed that a Christian colleague had occasionally been unavailable because he was 'at a Bible study'. From that time John had determined that he would only speak of his faith at work if asked about it.

He was very humble about his deft fingers which he used to display and deal with many a difficult surgical field. He worked extremely hard, kept a close eye on his junior colleagues, and made sure we felt well supported on the wards in the clinical decisions we made. On one occasion, knowing I was a Christian, he paged me on my bleep: 'Graham, I'm about to lose my temper; please pray that I don't'. 'I will, Mr Marsh.' And he put the phone down. He later informed me that my prayer had been answered.

After I had worked there for some time another of the junior doctors was talking to me about John Marsh and complimenting his skills: '... and he's a committed Christian you know' he said. There was no doubt that the life of the man had brought credit to his Lord. I met many patients who had been given self-worth simply by the gentle surgical expertise of John Marsh.

But later in life in discussions I had with him, he regretted that he hadn't opened up the topic of faith issues with patients more often. We need a balance. 'Preach the Gospel always, and if necessary, use words' [113] as the saying goes or 'What you do speaks so loud that I cannot hear what you are say' [114]? A lousy Christian life certainly makes any accompanying message hard for the hearer to understand. The Christian who serves well can look out for opportunities to see if the patient would find the faith perspective helpful.

Don't underestimate the importance of the impact of your life. 'Some day Tennyson's lines will be true, that our character is a part of all we have met.' [115] John Marsh's kindness, along with the warm hospitality of his wife, Elizabeth, was infectious and indeed he became a part of those he trained. His frequent chuckle, for example on one occasion at finding the junior doctors watching *Doctor Who* on TV in the doctors' sitting room, comes to me now as I write.

THE RESOLUTION TO CARE

Clinicians vary in their ability to communicate their caring concern
to patients. In one hospital where I worked one senior doctor was
renowned for the fact that when the patient was ushered into his
presence he wouldn't look at them or ask them anything, but study the
laboratory reports, the scan and X-ray results and then announce 'We'll
send for you'. It was then up to the harassed outpatient nurse to get
the patient out of the room! Thankfully most clinicians can manage
somewhat more patient-centred care than that. Expressing the empathy
we feel requires practice and sensitivity to the individual patient's needs.

But supposing we don't feel concerned for the patient, is it possible to
fake it? You would have to be an excellent actor to fake good care when
you are very busy and tired. But there is a sense in which good manners
are the determination to treat everyone equally well, no matter how I
am feeling or how tired I am. In a sense it is the decision to care, made
in advance, which gives the discipline to show empathy. It is often
remarkable how the act of caring and listening then leads to the genuine
heartfelt concern and, yes, love for the patient. This is an example of
feelings following decision. It is a sign of our determination to be
changed with God's help and to become what we should be, part
of being a work in progress.

The resolution to care, whether one feels like it or not, is a particular
mark of Christlikeness. Jesus actually despised his own suffering
because of the joy that he saw coming, [116] the rescue of people
everywhere who otherwise had cut themselves off from God's
lifegiving love.

GRATEFUL HUMILITY

If we do manage an outstanding quality of work and care in medicine,
but there is no explanation for this excellence, then it can condemn
others or become a dangerous ego trip for ourselves. A good life
unexplained is a bad teacher. For example, there is a danger that people
coming into our church with its tidily dressed people, its order and its
beautiful music may have the impression that Christians are really
personally sorted out, a state that to the observer seems unattainable.

Alternatively we may be seen as a bunch of hypocrites hiding the truth about ourselves under a veneer of religiosity. In the case of the former the observer feels merely condemned and in the case of the latter the observer feels vindicated. The smartly dressed Christian doctor who appears to know what she is doing may inspire confidence but may also induce the above reactions – 'I could never be as good as you' or 'it's alright for you, you've got a secure job and a good income'. We need to learn to bridge this gap.

The secret is a profound sense that we are just a bunch of ordinary people who have been rescued after having comprehensively failed to live by God's standards, who are responding out of grateful hearts, and who know that day by day we are utterly dependent on God.

MEETING JESUS IN THE PATIENT

The Franciscan perspective on clinical encounters is eminently expressed by Daniel Sulmasy. [117] He invites us to consider that when we encounter a patient we are in one sense meeting Jesus. Made in the image of God, however spoilt, there are glimpses of Jesus in the patient or staff which we can not only recognise and serve, but which can also help us.

On numerous occasions of course, it is I who have received care from the patients. This can be seen as Jesus meeting us through God's image in our patients. In July 2005 I was consulting in surgery in Sheffield. At that time my daughter was working teaching English to international students at Piccadilly Circus in the centre of London, to which she commuted by Tube. I came out to call in my next patients, a couple from Saudi Arabia, but the receptionist said that there had been explosions in the centre of London. It was the morning of the Tube bombings. Like thousands of others, my immediate reaction was to try to call my daughter on her mobile phone but the system was off. The Saudi couple came in to the consulting room. They had heard the news and immediately said 'Doctor, this is not an easy time for you, it is no problem, we'll come back another day'.

Their manner was warm and sympathetic. There was mature understanding about the anxiety. Suddenly they were the people I

actually wanted to be with me at that moment. What was it? Our
shared humanity in uncertainty and grief, somehow made more precious
by the fact we were patently from different religions and cultures. At
this moment, God's gift was the right people for me. In that context it
was easy to acknowledge the emotional interruption and then to attend
to their needs. At about midday, as soon as the phones were live again,
I had a call from my daughter – she was fine. Relief was tinged with
the grief that I knew was stabbing other parents' hearts at that moment.
The next week the Saudi couple returned to the surgery with anxious
concern: 'What news of your daughter – is she OK?'

On another occasion, having heard I was to have an operation on my
knee, a patient dropped off a spare pair of crutches for me at the surgery.

Similarly, colleagues can 'be Jesus' to each other in serving each other.
Working together in a supportive team in general practice or hospital
medicine can be a good place to experience the nurture of colleagues.
A young female patient had poured out her torrid tale of abuse and a
loveless home. After she left the immense tragedy of her plight overwhelmed
me and I wept. As I sat snorting into a rather soggy tissue, one of the
receptionists brought in a mug of coffee. 'I'm so sorry, I shouldn't have
come in' she said. 'No' said I, 'perfect timing: just what I need'. We
certainly get through a lot of tissues in my work (and a lot of coffee).

'SALVE'

Shortly after the death of my mother, herself a former GP, I was
discussing the nature of our respective vocations with my siblings. It
got me reflecting on what was really the essence of my own work as a
Christian GP. Now I'm not one much given to visions or dreams, though
I think God enjoys a huge range of ways of getting through to us. That
night I dreamed I was standing discussing with a group of people the
essence of my role. What was the heart of Jesus' role for me as a
Christian GP; how could it be summed up in a word? As we discussed
in the dream I said I didn't know. Then a woman in the group turned to
me and I knew she had an answer, but I didn't know what it was. She
paused, then said 'Salve'. I awoke. I only had a very vague notion of
what the word meant.

It turns out that salve has several meanings. As a noun it is soothing medication, a balm, applied to ease pain. As a verb it is to apply such ointment, but is also used in the sense 'to rescue from ruin, as in salvage'. And the complete rescue that Jesus has won for his disciples is known as salvation. Perhaps our role as Christian medics is to become salve for our patients.

In the book of Revelation Jesus says: 'You say, "I am rich: I have acquired wealth and do not need a thing." But you do not realise that you are wretched, pitiful, poor, blind and naked. I counsel you to buy from me gold refined in the fire, so that you can become rich; and white clothes to wear, so that you can cover your nakedness; and salve to put on your eyes, so you can see.' [118]

What a wonderful concept – the idea that we can have a whole new way of seeing things as they truly are from God's perspective, with our motives in looking cleaned up, and a fresh appreciation of the wonders of creation. I suppose this is also sight to appreciate just how destructive evil is, as well as insight that can help our patients.

REDRESS PATIENTS

We are familiar with the sensitivities of the physical examination in the consulting room. The patient voluntarily submits himself to an examination so that a correct diagnosis can be made. The examination involves an exposure of the physical self. The patient undresses and then redresses to expose the relevant part of their body. But we often forget that the history taking itself exposes the patient, the hurts, the fears, the vulnerabilities and even the odd strange ideas about disease. It can be embarrassing to parade one's ignorance or fears in front of an expert.

It is well to remember that in sharing these things a patient is exposing themselves to your clinical gaze. So we are to redress them psychologically before they leave the room. Give them some 'white clothes' to wear. There are numerous ways to do this. One way would be to acknowledge the privilege of serving in a consultation. Another would be to use their name in farewell. Find a form of words which you feel comfortable with. I tend to use it as a response to their thank you – something like

'And thank you for explaining it all to me so helpfully, Mrs Jones' or 'Thank you for giving me the privilege of hearing these confidences, Albert'. This is a 'salve' because it helps them to see themselves as the valuable people they are.

USING OUR OWN SUFFERING

The experience of suffering on the part of another person can be a very powerful help in illness. This person who has similarly suffered may be a friend, relative, doctor or nurse. Patients seek out others who have undergone similar illnesses, not just for practical tips but also for the fellowship of the community of suffering. Speaking of the value as a Christian of his experiences of cancer, journalist Soo Ewe Jin said 'My experience has certainly made me a better counsellor to those who are beginning the same journey. I am able to offer advice that is practical and useful, and speak words of comfort that don't sound hollow.' [119] The Christian medic can and should use any suffering he or she has endured to comfort patients when appropriate.

TAKING RISKS

Salve is not just a matter of comfort. Sometimes unusual things happen:

A DOCTOR'S STORY

'I'd rather stand if it's OK with you, Doc.' I had watched Ahmed walk fairly cautiously into the consulting room. 'I think it's piles, Doc.' Sure enough it was piles. Prolapsed, thrombosed, and very painful. He had been in increasing agony with difficulty walking for two weeks.

'Tell me about it: what were you doing when they came on?' I asked. 'Have you got a few minutes, Doc?' And so the story came out. A few years previously on a visit to his country of birth he had, on one occasion, met the wife of a wealthy landowner. Nothing had happened between them, but about six months ago Ahmed was told that the landowner had put a price on his head. The landowner believed that his wife had had an affair with Ahmed. The landowner's honour was at stake.

Ahmed was well known to me over a number of years. A Muslim, he was happily married and a taxi driver with young children. He was a tower of support to some disabled relatives. Then he had discovered that his life was being threatened. Some people had been sent to hunt him down. He had been desperate; he knew what this landowner was capable of. He hadn't told his wife and he feared for his children. He had decided there was only one way out: to take the law into his own hands. So he gathered a posse of friends to go and kill the landowner before he was killed first. He returned to that country and spent two weeks with his friends playing cat and mouse with his enemy – there was a lot of shooting, but thankfully no one got hurt. Then in the midnight dashes between hotels and fast car chases, Ahmed developed an acute attack of piles. He couldn't move quickly. He had to abort the attack and return home. The piles were only one problem; the other problem was that the landowner was still alive.

'Ahmed, may I make a suggestion?' I said. 'Go ahead, Doc.'
'I think God is speaking to you through your piles.' We laughed.
'No, actually I mean it!' 'Well then, what do you think he's saying?'

I explained that God loved him and this landowner and didn't want either of them dead or a family feud to start. The piles had possibly saved both his and the landowner's life. Now the situation had to be resolved. God himself would show him the way through if he was willing. Would he forgive the man? Certainly. Would he be willing to apologise for even the appearance of an affair? Certainly. He also told me that he knew the landowner himself was now really scared. I asked what might he do to effect a reconciliation?

On the next visit he told me that he had made contact through an intermediary and opened negotiations. Then he had actually spoken with his adversary on the phone. He had apologised. They had agreed that Ahmed would take gifts (including a cow!) to a feast at which they would be seen to be friends – an important signal to their respective supporters. Ahmed asked me to pray for his safety. A few weeks later Ahmed disappeared for some time and then returned reporting that it had all gone well. Honour was satisfied. He no

> *longer even needed the ointment for his piles! And he has since asked me a lot of questions about Jesus.*

It was an understanding of his worldview by the doctor that helped him find a way through the *impasse*. But it was only the doctor's faith in a redeeming God that meant he could respond sincerely at that critical moment. Here we have people with different worldviews using some shared truth about God to come to a resolution of a problem. This doesn't mean that the Christian thought that Islam is totally true or vice versa. But the Christian doctor respected the Muslim's position and then highlighted forgiveness and the need for an exercise of faith, and left the next steps to the patient. Both patient and clinician learnt something about God. The patient knew the doctor was a Christian and so the exchange has left Christ honoured even though Christ's name hasn't been mentioned.

Eugene Peterson [120] reminded us that when Nicodemus approached Jesus at night he did so at risk to his personal reputation, and when Jesus spoke with a woman at a well in Samaria he did so at the risk of his reputation. Similarly for us, there are occasions when patients take major risks in exposing their problems to us, and occasions when we will risk our reputation seeking to be Christlike in the healthcare setting. Knowing the right time to take the risk can require great wisdom.

So is it possible to be like Jesus? Just being there is already an imitation of Christ; listening and identifying with the suffering; providing lucid insights into the heart of the problem and encouraging the steps that are needed; affirming the immense value of the individual and community; being willing to make sacrifices in servanthood; taking risks. And occasionally pointing to God, for ultimately it is only God who can restore life itself.

13. BUILDING SELF-WORTH AND DEALING WITH GUILT

AN OPHTHALMOLOGIST'S STORY

I was working in Eye Casualty when a social worker brought a 13 year old boy who had allegedly been assaulted by his father. 'What happened to you?' I asked. 'My Dad hit me' came the reply. The enormity of the pain of the situation hit me like a slap in the face and I felt a surge of anger and emotion.

Taking control of myself, I took a full history which revealed intermittent drug use ('Hash [marijuana] and base [crack cocaine] when I can get it') and examined the boy, who mercifully had no more than a subconjunctival haemorrhage. I had the report typed immediately. As we parted I said to the boy: 'You are worth a great deal more than you think, try to take care of yourself'.

In his hard-hitting review of attitudes and behaviours in *Life at the bottom* Theodore Dalrymple [121] attacks the way modern thought and the welfare state combine to imprison lower socioeconomic groups in vicious circles of low self-esteem, violence, the derision of excellence, victimhood and perverted 'love'. Drawn from Dalrymple's experience as a prison doctor, it makes for a grim commentary. Much of what he says is echoed in my experience as an inner city GP in the UK, though I'd come to different conclusions.

BUYING SELF-WORTH

Where do our patients look for value or self-worth today? One instant answer is shopping, purchasing desirable objects that make the owner feel good. The adverts shout that you need this or that to fulfil your life (hidden message: happiness can be bought, your value lies in being a consumer). We are bombarded day by day with images of unattainable bodily perfection, desirable goods, and even better holidays, in the adverts of a capitalist society. So much relies on us being discontented. The feelgood factor lasts for such a short time; we are soon back for more. Insatiable greed distorts the blessings of mutual trade. Is it surprising that we live in a discontented society? Pity the politicians who will never be able to satisfy the selfish egoism of the discontented consumer.

It is amazing that those who can least afford material goods will often put themselves into deep debt to buy those 'must have' items as a sign that they have moved on from a squalid or worthless past. This is designer self-worth with the irony that it comes with the label 'consumer'. As Bishop James Jones has pointed out, how tragic and ironic is the label 'consumer'. [122] Consumer is a dehumanising label that suggests one who devours and destroys all it desires with a voracious and insatiable appetite – what an identity to acquire in response to advertisements and low self-esteem. There are some encouraging signs that some in the younger generation are rejecting the acquisition of excess material goods, realising that possessions often come to possess and control the owner, rather than the other way round. For the Christian these objects and experiences aren't bad in themselves – in fact most are the good gifts of God in an extraordinary creation. But once the idea is lost that they are the gifts of a loving creator, then they don't themselves confer lasting self-worth. It is the idea that they are gifts that has this potential. They are then the 'come on' from a heavenly Father who knows better than we do how to give good gifts. If we know how to give good gifts, how much more does an all wise God. [123] More than disappointment with selfish enjoyment, gratitude to God for gifts leaves us hungry and hopeful for the perfect gift that we may get glimpses of in this life, to beckon us into a relationship where 'moth and rust don't corrupt' [124] – or batteries run down.

RANK

Another powerful source of self-worth is rank (or status as we discussed in Chapter 8). Rank is the way people in different societies are ordered according to importance. It is of variable significance in different cultures, and an understanding of what conveys rank may help avoid misunderstandings in multicultural practice. For example, in one country where I worked the polite first question was to ask how much you earned and how much your house cost – this enabled the new friend to establish a rank relationship with you which was based on financial worth.

Generally in the UK this line of questioning would not be a good idea! Unemployment is often a stigma, and particularly people who are coming out of employment will make strenuous efforts to conceal their joblessness. Employment is one of many factors that people take into account in various ways in different societies to determine a perception of rank. A doctor in the UK has traditionally had high rank. Other attributes such as being married with children, university educated, white, and having English as a first language would be considered by others as conferring rank. Often the person with the high rank doesn't notice it, so it may be easy to forget that it is the other person who is sensitive to what they think they lack. This can create an automatic barrier which the doctor or nurse or receptionist will need to make an extra effort to overcome. It is naturally easier to converse with people like oneself. Often I am seen initially as yet another authority figure. Because of rank it is easy in the first few moments of contact to undermine self-worth with a lack of welcome.

RELATIONSHIPS AND SELF WORTH

And then there is the major source of self-worth: relationships. This is what had been violated for our 13 year old patient in the story above. The child who is secure and treasured from before birth has a foundation of security in their own value that immediately places them at an advantage. It is the certainty of being loved, of being accepted and of belonging.

The child, like the 13 year old, who is habitually knocked about will develop a deep sense of low self-esteem. After all he knows he irritates his Dad, so guilt and false guilt mix with anger. His Dad's own lack of self-control makes the son also feel powerless and a victim. If his Dad isn't responsible for his own behaviour, how can he be? He may seek the approval of his peers as a substitute relationship, and drugs follow with the emotional escape they offer. Paradoxically some children in this situation see the violence as a sign of love. The logic works like this: 'Dads love their children, Dad hits me, therefore hitting me must be a sign of love' and this can progress to: 'if he doesn't hit me he doesn't love me'. [125] There is a hidden perverted truth in this – if a parent truly loves a child they will be concerned for their safety and that they reach their full potential, and some discipline in a home is an essential ingredient to a healthy upbringing. I have come across intelligent adults who thought that violence in the home was entirely normal, as they had never witnessed anything else and assumed all families were violent.

I have seen plenty of parents where the reverse is true and I have pointed out to the parents of an overly fussy eater aged three: 'Who is the leader in this house? Is a three year old really the boss? You will make her very insecure if she feels she is in control and then gets it wrong.' But this need for loving leadership in a home is a million miles away from the abuse of the self-centred parent who lashes out, often under the influence of alcohol. And in the bottle there is another hidden message: 'to my father a bottle of cider is worth more than I am'.

Girls who have suffered abuse in childhood often develop relationships in adulthood with partners who abuse them. Sometimes they have actually come to believe that true love should be expressed by displaying paranoid jealousy or by being violently controlling. Indeed the partner who treats their opinion and plans with respect and gentleness may be seen as a wimp and as not really caring.

Violent male partners are extremely unlikely to change while in a relationship, though the female often clings to the belief that he'll change and that she'll be the agent of the transformation. Maybe our 13 year old's mother was in this situation. Perhaps our 13 year old was even taking the aggression to protect her. These are the tragically common scenarios faced by GPs and social workers in our cities.

On many occasions I have urged a woman to flee from a violent relationship. After many people had implored one young lady to leave her violent man she had eventually realised what danger she was in when, holding his hands around her neck, he dangled her from the balcony of a high rise maisonette in the presence of her young child. She wisely moved cities, presented herself and her children as homeless, and was placed in a hostel at a secret location pending rehousing.

JESUS CHRIST AND SELF-WORTH

Building self-worth is essential because it empowers the patient to take what control they can. The most potent way to do this is with the Christian good news – the story of a creator God who has worked for millennia on this universe, who loves each one of us so passionately that he demonstrates his love by lowering himself in Jesus Christ to the form of a servant to suffer and take the consequences of our evil, so that we can enjoy a love relationship with him if we want to and live forever. This is an astounding statement of the value of each human.

SHARING WEAKNESS

One way to even the rank issue between healthcare worker and patient is to admit that we are all human and we all make mistakes – a little simple honesty about our shared humanity. I have a routine with drug addicts and it seems to help. Most feel an intense sense of worthlessness. This is hardly surprising: one will have stolen money from his grandmother to buy heroin, or another will have lost contact with her children because of addiction, or for another a friend has died on the end of a needle which they were administering. When you add this to the low self-esteem from abusive childhoods one is sometimes amazed that they survive at all.

Addiction occurs when a rapid biochemical reward is delivered to the brain very soon after some stimulus. It is natural to seek that pleasure or that escape again. The problem with heroin is that the body's own endorphins get suppressed so that a chemical as well as a psychological dependency ensues. Most people have felt the force of an addictive habit: over-eating, alcohol, anorexia, smoking, pornography. Addiction is a strange thing. One of my patients described how every time she heard the tram approaching in the street she'd get the same rush she had as if she was injecting herself with heroin. This was because the drug dealer usually visited her by tram.

Another of my patients, a former drug addict, found himself surprised to have a continuing urge to shoplift because of the adrenaline rush.

This is rather reminiscent of St Augustine [126] who as a lad used to steal pears, not to eat them, but for the pleasure of doing what was forbidden. With most addictions the psychological reward lessens over time, but by this time people find themselves trapped. As Jesus said, 'Everyone who sins is a slave to sin'. [127] So sometimes I tell patients that there is a shop not far from the clinic selling pornographic material – I have consciously to 'eyes front' as I walk past. We are all vulnerable and weak. As the saying goes 'Sow a thought, reap an act; sow an act, reap a habit; sow a habit, reap a character; sow a character, reap a destiny'. [128] Isn't it strange that temptation always has the appearance of offering freedom but actually enslaves, while virtue has the appearance of control but is actually liberating? To escape the one and find the other we all need a miracle of change. 'If the Son sets you free, you will be free indeed.' [129]

ENCOURAGEMENT

One step towards helping patients grasp the possibility of change is to look for the positives in their character and then give them feedback. Somewhere near the end of the consultation I ask: 'Do you mind if tell you something I've noticed about you?' (That usually grabs their attention!) I then say something like this: 'I have seen literally thousands of patients. We have never met before. What I notice about you is that you explained your problem well – you are a good communicator, and you have taken good care of your appearance, and you have a sense of humour even though things are tough at present – I think you are worth more than you think you are. Don't give up on yourself.'

Obviously it is key that the observations are true. This is a point at which the doctor or nurse can use the authority of their office to bless. I have found that my patients are uniformly pleasantly surprised (this is not the sort of thing Britons tend to say to each other!) and you can see confidence growing. With confidence comes empowerment and the ability to take action. And this is what our ophthalmologist was doing with his 13 year old – grabbing the brief opportunity given to him. He told me that the encounter had stayed on his heart and so he had turned his thoughts into prayer to God.

DEALING WITH GUILT

A GP'S STORY

A 54 year old cleaner, Anne, whom I'd known for five years, came to see me with two problems. She was already on an antidepressant for long standing depression and thyroxine for her underactive thyroid gland. I greeted her and after she sat down she told me her sleep had deteriorated and secondly she had attacks of a 'horrible shivering sensation' which passed over her whole body. She was very frustrated by the lack of sleep and hated the shivering attacks which happened several times a day.

After she'd told me about it, I looked at her and my first question was: 'Are you feeling guilty about something by any chance?' I thought 'the hobnail boots approach – this is a risk I can take because she knows me – but it is high risk, she might be offended'. I had tried to couch it in a mischievous tone of voice with a smile, to soften the impact. She smiled: 'Oh! Well! Six weeks ago I smacked my 30 year old daughter in the face. I have never done that before, and she hasn't spoken to me since. Ooohh! I'm having one of those horrible shivers now!'

It turned out that her daughter had a new boyfriend of whom Anne absolutely disapproved and they had had a row, culminating in the slap. 'So how long have you had the problem with sleep and the shivers?' I asked, but I thought I already knew the answer. 'Six weeks.' 'Well, maybe...' 'No, I think it's either a side-effect of my antidepressants or perhaps my thyroxine levels.'

We agreed to tackle the problem at all levels. We checked the blood thyroxine levels, adjusted the dose of the antidepressant, and discussed what she thought she might do about the relationship with her daughter. We discussed issues of ownership – who owned her daughter? What should a parent do who disapproves of a grown-up child's choice of partner? She decided that while she was right to warn her daughter about this man, she should apologise for the slap and say she wanted to keep a relationship, not least for the sake of any possible future grandchildren.

*'Is there anything else you could do?' I asked. 'Well, I suppose
I could pray for them.' 'Good idea.'*

*It actually took about four visits to see me, satisfactory blood tests, and
even a follow-up with the endocrinologist (who discharged her) before
one day she said with a grin, 'You know, I think it's all to do with my
daughter'. A few months later Anne attended for review. 'You look
really well and relaxed' I said, and then with a smile, 'How's that
daughter of yours?' 'Away in South America for six weeks!'*

*We laughed. A few years later she was helping the couple with the
care of her grandchildren. One reason I recall this sequence so well
is because I don't usually ask about guilt as my first question! Also
my Bible reading that day had spoken of insomnia and guilt.
Was it a hunch, or the leading of the Holy Spirit? I think God
is keener to help than we imagine.*

Should we ask about people's consciences more? With Anne, the GP
was taking a risk because she knew her and Anne trusted her to try
genuinely to help. God the Father wants us to understand his heart of
compassion as we appreciate just how much he loves us and others, and
to cultivate those two necessary skills of the good medic: curiosity and
empathy.

Then there is the question of correct attribution. A doctor, and
especially a Christian doctor, seeks to attribute a patient's symptoms
correctly to their cause or causes. Leading a patient to understand the
truth of the diagnosis is often tricky. Knowing my own slowness to learn
helps me be patient. Anne was slow to grasp the truth of her symptoms
and found it hard to accept that emotional causes can give rise to bodily
symptoms. Once she accepted the attribution and took action, her
symptoms resolved. Even if the symptoms are untreatable, correct
attribution of symptoms can be an immense relief to a patient. So a
patient with past cancer may assume that flu symptoms represent a
recurrence and can be immensely relieved by the doctor's reassurance.

In Anne's case the order of the consultation was unusual but useful. The
history shortcut at the start was a potentially powerful moment. But still

the process of correct attribution took several weeks. Would a more gradual approach have been more convincing? Perhaps the suddenness of the 'eureka' moment was a bit too quick for her. But however it worked out, the issue of guilt or conscience was key. Perhaps other open questions may have drawn it out. On many occasions I have asked people 'Is there anything else bothering you, anything on your conscience?' Sometimes the flood gates open and sometimes I receive a simple 'No'. Even that 'No' may be a defence when there is a 'Yes' inside, and the patient may reappear or go elsewhere to deal with it later after consideration.

If a patient mentions guilty feelings I will often draw a diagram dividing

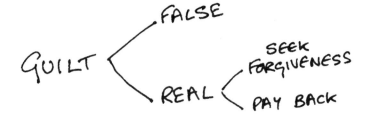

DEALING WITH FALSE GUILT

False guilt needs identifying for what it is. It is usually easy for patients to understand transfer of guilt and false guilt in child abuse situations. The abusing adult tells the child it is their fault, or that they're bad, or in some other way the abused child is made to feel it is their fault. This false guilt can be compounded if the abuser is sent to prison, commits suicide, or the family is broken up as a result of revelations about abuse.

As an adult later they can appreciate the duty of protection an adult has towards a child and realise that these guilt feelings and this sense of being dirty have been imposed on them by others. But even then the eradication of the accusatory voices from the past seems remarkably difficult. The patient has to identify the false guilt and face up to it as being fundamentally a lie. This is not easy when you have been treated as an object for the release of another's lust or anger, or treated as less important than a bottle of alcohol or a fix of drugs.

There are many other situations where false guilt is important to recognise – for example, parenting is never straightforward and it easy for children to manipulate their parents by inducing false guilt. This might be by comparing parenting, for example: 'But James' parents always give him a lift to the sports hall twice a week and you always make me take the bus'. Parents with mental health issues can really struggle with this sort of thing.

DEALING WITH REAL GUILT

Real guilt is dealt with by change, forgiveness and restitution. Awareness of real guilt occurs when we begin to grasp the cost of the evil for which we have been responsible. We come to understand its painful effect on others and the community, its tendency to multiply, its deadening of our enjoyment of life. Developing a patient's awareness of consequences of their actions may be a powerful motivator to change.

When a habitual drug user comes asking for help with referral for drug detoxification, the initial questions include motivation – for example, 'Why do you want to detox? Why now?' Frequently the reasons are because of a realisation of consequences – a girlfriend is threatening to end the relationship, or a court is requiring evidence of improvement before allowing access to children, or a grandmother not seen for several years has died still grieving over her lost grandchild. I press on: are there other reasons? 'I'm too old for this game, I need to settle down.' I press on: what about hopes for the future? Maybe the patient wants to enroll in a course, or have a family, or get back to regular work. One homeless patient surprised me by saying 'I'd really like to be a volcanologist'!

Finally, when the patient can give no more reasons, I ask if I may add a few. I then mention the lives wrecked by the illicit drugs trade round the world, the theft, the murder, the intimidation, the organised crime, the terrorism, the landmines, the children maimed: these are the real casualties of this addiction. There is a real chain of evil in this mess. The patients are often surprised. So am I. Why is there so *little* stigma attached to this evil in our society? I remember a hard hitting anti-drugs campaign in Malaysia. The posters had a single word *dadah* (illicit drugs) written in faeces.

This said, I want to encourage the patient that they are not alone. We all have addictions causing varying degrees of harm. We all need to change, we all need forgiveness, and we are all in it together. We discuss how the patient might find forgiveness from those hurt. We discuss how a life of restitution looks. Finally, if the patient gives permission, I describe how I believe that God, as owner of all, has the right to forgive and how justice is satisfied at the Cross, and how he gives the strength to change.

There is so much evil, so much suffering. If you have never shed tears in your clinic or your hospital, may I ask why not? Do you not sometimes wonder why a good God lets it all go on? In this brief time we have an opportunity to respond to God's offer of free forgiveness and be changed. God is not slow, but patient. [130] Restitution is the action which demonstrates the change of heart.

A NURSE'S STORY

A young man attended for a new patient medical. During the consultation I had to leave the room for a moment to get an additional form we needed. The consultation ended without event. A few days later I was rather surprised to see him again. He produced a ten pound note and said 'This is yours. I stole it from your handbag last time, but you were so kind to me I felt guilty and want you to have it back. I suppose you'll have to tell the doctors and they'll cancel the registration, but that's OK.' I took this issue to the practice meeting and it was decided that the patient could certainly remain, and staff were reminded to take care not to leave temptation in people's way!

This was real repentance. The kindness of the nurse won the affection of the thief. One young addict I saw was grieved that his grandmother had died before he'd come clean from his drugs and wanted to do something. He knew she loved him and would have forgiven him. 'In future,' said I, 'You could look out for old women and take special care of them.' I don't know if he did. But I hope it was one step towards discovering grace.

To be forgiven is to be valued more than the offence, as the young man in our story found. To be forgiven is to be liberated from debt. So God's forgiveness confers value and freedom. This is not cost-free justice as God himself pays the price. Through the experience of being forgiven and of forgiving others we learn what true forgiveness is. Then we can't hold on to resentment. Resentment is the determination to feel again the pain inflicted upon us. 'Our capacity to forgive, the ease, speed and endurance of our forgiveness are related to our level of self-esteem.' [131]

A GP'S STORY

One of my female patients suffered terrible abuse at the hands of her uncle when she was four. He persistently told her she was evil and that it was her fault. Her mother failed to protect her initially but then moved away with my patient when she was seven. Due to a legal mix-up the prosecution of her uncle failed and he never faced trial.

As a young woman my patient married a violent man who abused her and the child he had by her. She failed to protect her daughter and initially colluded with her partner who went to prison. False guilt and real guilt, anger and resentment all combine to give very low self-worth. Her daughter, now an adult, won't speak to her. Not surprisingly she suffers from low mood and sleeplessness. She has hurt herself often in the past.

Over the years one of our tasks has been to assure her repeatedly of her value, her courage in persevering, and her gifts in communication and listening to others. Slowly, very slowly, she is emerging. She has not yet found it in herself to forgive her uncle, and perhaps not herself, but for the first time in years she has begun smiling.

A GP'S STORY

I was talking to one of my patients who is gay and who really struggles with long term anxiety. 'Tell me,' I asked, 'has religious faith played much of a part in your life?' 'I know you're a Christian, doctor, but to be honest I rather gave up on church in my teens.' His experience of church had not been good.

'Well, John, can I just say one thing? I don't think Jesus has given up on you.' After that he pestered me for a Christian book I'd mentioned until I got it for him.

14. DO NOT BE AFRAID

A GP'S STORY

A 24 year old student, a new patient, consulted me with a minor illness and said, 'while I'm here can I have my repeat prescription?' He was on medication for chronic anxiety. 'How is the anxiety these days?' I asked.

'After a lot of thought I decided what I really wanted to do, and have recently moved here to study radiotherapy. What I hadn't expected is that the course is actually tending to make the anxiety worse.' 'Which part of the course is causing the trouble, is it seeing so many cancer patients?' 'No, it's not the time with the patients – I enjoy that. It's the study time reading all about the cancers in the evenings.'

I then suggested to him that his anxiety had two main components: a wild imagination out of control and wrong believing. Someone with a strong imagination is more susceptible to anxiety. As far as wrong believing is concerned, I explained that wrong believing could consist of a poor assessment of the real risk. Maybe one way would be to face the reality of the problem and proceed with actual knowledge if possible. For example, he could find out the actual incidence of the cancer of which he was fearful, and the weighting of the risk factors,

and try and place this in the context of other known risks.
Then I explained that one's view of the universe would also play a
part: is this a random world where we could be crushed by some
incident at any moment, or is there a loving God behind creation
and, despite suffering, in the end 'all will be well'. Clearly, I said,
one's view of the world can have a big influence on anxiety. He
laughed and nodded. 'I'm a Christian, and I know I should stay
more centred on Jesus.' 'So am I. I think that would be good.'
(I wish I'd then asked: 'How might you do that?')

In his honest account of his own journey through cancer, Fear No Evil, David
Watson reflected on the ways fellow believers had responded to suffering in
the past. [132] He wrote: 'Christians down the ages have discovered the
'treasures of darkness' and have gained a richness of maturity and spirituality
that would have been impossible when the sun was shining.' His own story
demonstrates this as he describes his reactions and fears in the face of his last
illness. He shares the fragility of his emotions alongside his growing intimacy
with God. To him the opposite of faith was not doubt: doubts honestly
expressed are part of faith; no, the opposite of faith is fear.

There are many ways of analysing and treating fear and I'm very grateful
for the psychotherapists and psychiatrists who have worked steadily
with the patients we have referred to them. In this chapter I'm sharing
some examples, and my own perspectives on fear.

To go back to the rope bridge example again: I may have doubts about
that rope bridge, and check it out before crossing – that is simple
wisdom. But fear may stop me walking onto the bridge at all. I stare
at the roaring cataract below and imagine tumbling to death among the
rocks. Inappropriate fear can cause us to lose sight of truth, of the guide
who has crossed ahead beckoning me over.

Fear is bad: it can be paralysing. Anxiety like this can cause people
to waste their lives utterly. I have patients who stay indoors all day
because going out makes them feel so awful. It also manifests itself
in ways other than the classic agitation and panic attacks. Defensive,
avoidant, and aggressive behaviour can flow from it. Sometimes the
anxiety is actually not focused on something terrible but merely on

the vile sensation of the nervousness. Panic about feeling panicky.
Fear of fear itself – a truly tragic trap to have fallen into.

I use two simple ways of looking at fear with patients. One method is to
draw the circle of anxiety: increased adrenaline, fast heart rate, stomach
discomfort, dry mouth, breathlessness, sense of impending doom –
worsened anxiety.

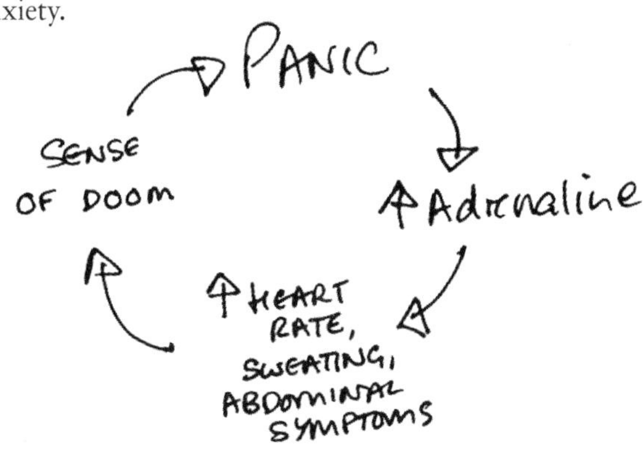

PANIC

SENSE
OF DOOM

↑ Adrenaline

↑ HEART
RATE,
SWEATING,
ABDOMINAL
SYMPTOMS

Once the patient understands the vicious circle of anxiety, it is possible
to teach the reversal of the process. The patient needs to grasp the
erroneous thoughts that lead to the anxiety, the harmlessness of the
feelings of the body getting ready for 'flight or fight', and identify
suitable physical activity to abate the symptoms or, sometimes,
appropriate medication.

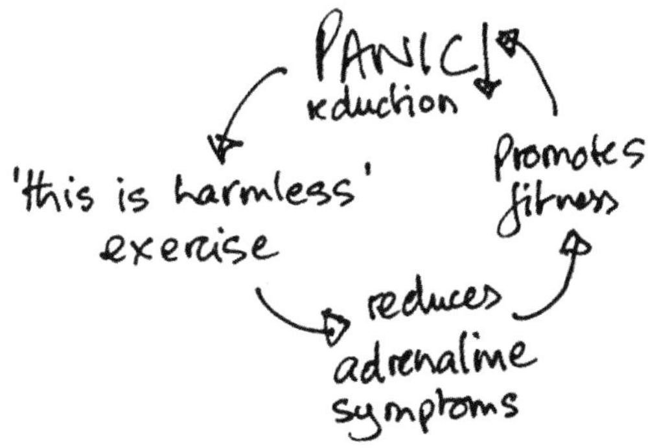

PANIC
reduction

'this is harmless'
exercise

promotes
fitness

reduces
adrenaline
symptoms

I sometimes advise patients that they shouldn't spend too much time
worrying – life is too short! Well, at least that gives them something
significant to worry about!

A GP's STORY

A retired professional couple came to see me about their cholesterol levels. They were very anxious to know the exact levels and the ratio of the different types of cholesterol. Over several visits they went into great detail about the side effects of possible medication, the many studies debating the merits of various regimes, and the complexities of their diet. They were increasingly obsessed and anxious. Finally, perhaps rather out of impatience, I reminded them that life was short at best: what were they living for? What did they hope to achieve? Where was God in all of this?

I rather feared that I would get told off for daring to speak to such obviously knowledgeable and eminent people in this way, but they took it with great grace and went away very thoughtful. When they returned they informed me that they had decided to create community in the condominium where they lived. A few years later they were still at the hub of a thriving group of friends on that floor level in the block, where any newcomer was systematically welcomed and introduced into the group. Nowadays they are so taken up with the needs of others that they don't worry so much about the minutiae of their lives. Well, not quite so much – the husband still wants a regular screening blood test every year...

Another tool I use to discuss inappropriate fear is taken from a phrase I recall from an old sermon: 'fear is wild imagining and wrong believing'. [133] So I draw a diagram and discuss and note down what the patient imagines may happen. Then we examine wrong believing.

A GP'S STORY

Margaret, a 70 year old lady, suffered from long term anxiety. When she was ten she played breath holding games with her sister. They used to goad each other on with statements such as 'You'll never breathe again!' It seemed exciting but was also terrifying for Margaret. She developed a slight dry cough from time to time with a sensation in the neck that her breathing wasn't quite right.

Then at the age of 30 she nursed her father as he died of lung cancer. It was peaceful for him, but she found the sound of the moisture of his breathing very frightening. Her attempts to be sure to clear her throat by coughing became more insistent and she had it checked by consultants in ear, nose and throat diseases. She was always worrying about her symptoms and what they might mean. Despite her continuing cough and repeated negative investigations she was very happily married, but then her husband developed cancer of the oesophagus and after a few years of treatment died.

The sensation in the throat continued even worse and she sought the advice of many doctors. By this stage the habitual coughing had caused a chronic laryngitis which was not expected to improve. The symptoms varied from a lump in the throat, to chest discomfort, and back to dry cough. Margaret's 'wild imagining' had become deeply entrenched, her habit of perpetually trying to clear the cough had entrenched the laryngeal damage. The process of dealing with the 'wild imagining' is slow – three major life events have all suggested to her that dying from something blocking the throat may happen any time. Her resting thoughts often return to this.

WILD IMAGINATION

For many patients mentioning 'wild imagining' or 'an imagination out of control' brings a smile of recognition to the patient's face as he or she recognises a description that fits themselves. As with Margaret, this may be because they have endured a series of adverse events which they then generalise in their thinking to apply to themselves. They have a natural desire to avoid the unpleasant reminders. Sometimes they have seen unpleasant images in the media, or sometimes they just have a vivid imagination. Clarifying the fear itself may be liberating and the clinician may be able to dispel it – for example correcting a misconception as to how a certain disease may be caught.

WRONG BELIEF

The second part of the analysis of fear is 'wrong believing'. This may be simply a poor perception of risk, or what can be done about it. When people are terrified of something they can sometimes become more objective by thinking of another low risk situation causing fear. One illustration I have used is to say that there is a possibility that I'll be killed by a meteorite as I step out of the building. It is a real, but extremely small possibility. If I take this risk too seriously I'd never go outside again! The patient immediately understands the stupidity of this as a way of life.

So 'wrong believing' may be the pointlessness of worrying about a risk which we can't modify. Currently I don't have any obvious influence on the rocks in space. A clinician's work is often about clarifying risk, or balancing risks of different options with a patient – for example whether to prescribe antibiotics or not? Or whether to advise cholesterol lowering treatment or not? Or whether this chemotherapy is worth the side effects? All courses of action are associated with risk. Presenting risk in an intelligible form is our duty, even when patients are fearful of the truth and want the doctor to decide for them.

But a sense of ultimate risk is something different. It is of course a matter of worldview. Am I really safe? As I write a guest's son and daughter have been playing in our snowy garden. The boy comes in with excitement. Secure in his place in the family, enjoying the gift of the day, you can see he is confident in the love of his parents which he has no need to question. His job today is simple – to be a child. You can tell he is deeply secure.

So when discussing wrong believing it is a natural step to ask about the patient's view of ultimate risk. I would enquire about the patient's worldview if I didn't already know it. Exploring what the patient believes is critical in unravelling the fear. I have had patients who believe they are being punished or will be punished, or are possessed, or are under a curse. Sometimes I am astonished at what a patient is fearful of because it is possible to interpret illness in so many ways. Reading this it may sound as if it all takes a long time in the consulting room, but often just a brief question such as 'What is it you worry about most?' or 'What is your greatest fear?' can crystallise something and help the patient face it squarely.

A MISSIONARY DOCTOR'S STORY

We had been away and when we got home the housemaid told us that a sizeable cobra had settled itself around the coat hooks in our hallway. My husband and two friends worked out a strategy, and with the help of some safety apparel for us and then kerosene sprayed in its face and a large stick, the cobra was dispatched. Subsequent to this event, our housemaid became unwell. She was too weak to get up from her bed and lost her appetite. She deteriorated over a few days. Clinical examination shed no light on her illness so we decided she would need to be admitted to the local hospital for investigations. Rather as an afterthought, remembering that we were Christians, we offered to pray for her, asking that the hospital would sort out her illness.

To our surprise, following the prayer she made a rapid recovery and didn't go to the hospital. She explained that she had believed that the gods sometimes took the form of animals such as snakes and as the snake had been killed in the house she was convinced that vengeance would be wrought on her and she would die. After the prayer her fear lifted.

USEFUL FEAR

If the patient has a faith in God: what is he like? Is he good? Why do they think that? If there is a good God who loves us, who understands suffering when we don't and is with us in it, who can and ultimately will bring good out of evil, who offers a relationship and the possibility of a new body and life for ever beyond death – then ultimately who or what is there to be afraid of, except him? As the old hymn has it 'Fear him, ye saints, then ye will have nothing else to fear'. [134]

There is, naturally then, useful fear. It is wise to be afraid of a lion, or the possible impact of a London bus! But so often our fear is misdirected. It is inappropriate fear that is the enemy. I daresay in this year of 2011 many of us would be happy if certain bankers had been somewhat more fearful of ultimate accountability to their maker! We could wish that Idi Amin, or Stalin, or Hitler, or Pol Pot, or those who decimate the rain forests of Brazil, or those who poison our children with illicit drugs, or those who impose unjust trade rules on the poor, or those who condone corruption, or those who deny education to the needy – we could wish that these people had been more afraid of God. Coming judgment at God's throne is great news for all those who suffer under tyranny. Justice in this life, a good sign of what is to come, will only be partial at best. And if what Jesus said is true: I myself cannot escape this coming judgment. But I know that without him I too stand condemned – having often ignored the needs of those around me by ignorance, selfishness or sheer laziness.

If God exists then a right awe and reverence for him is what counts along with a response to his love. Then, secure in his love, the possibility of future suffering need not paralyse the present.

MARGARET'S STORY CONTINUED

I would like to be able to say that, having identified her fears and the source of her symptoms, we prayed and she was wonderfully healed. But this would not be true! She still has her symptoms which move about. She has had many examinations and scans repeatedly over the years. It has happened so many times there is a note on the computer to new doctors: 'Please look at old notes before re-referral'. She has faith in Christ. She enters the room with a smile and describes again the 'worst symptoms ever' and I may reflect to her that she has used this phrase before. She says 'I know it can't be cancer because I've had it so long, I just wish the sensation would go away'. On some occasions when she has been distressed I have given her a hug. I have prayed for her in her presence and given her reassuring Bible verses. She has tried numerous symptomatic remedies, antidepressants and psychotherapy.

My desire to find a cure remains, but in reality I have to settle for being weak and powerless and, with the team, just be alongside when needed; hopeful that we may find something useful, but expectant that the gift of a new transformed body after the resurrection will resolve all. Then, at last, she will breathe freely.

15. MENTAL HEALTH AND WORLDVIEW

M ental illness is complex and confusing at the best of times. The suffering can be atrocious. It is not surprising then that of all spheres of disease it is mental illness that is perhaps most likely to cause a crisis of worldview. This chapter is a brief collection of some ideas and stories around this subject. I have found that giving the patient a structure in which to understand their illness often seems useful.

A 26 year old woman came to me for a follow up appointment regarding her depression. Martha was a recruitment consultant, a challenging job in which she normally thrived. She lived alone but had a circle of good friends whom she spent time with. She attended to her physical health with regular trips to the gym. Despite all these positive aspects of her life her appetite was poor, her sleep was disturbed, and she felt flat. She couldn't work out why.

Once I had excluded physical causes of low mood a few weeks previously (I've been caught out by sinusitis before) she had agreed to try an antidepressant and had now come for review. Overall she was feeling slightly better. As she was standing at the door and about to leave she said, 'The thing is, I feel guilty because I haven't got any reason to be depressed – there are so many other people worse off than me'.

'Sit down again a moment' said I, 'that sounds like false guilt.
Your depression is probably mainly a matter of brain chemistry but...'
and I proceeded to tell her one way to think of mental illness.

Paul McHugh, a psychiatrist with Johns Hopkins University, outlined
a model of mental illness which I have found very helpful with patients. [135]
He identifies four factors for mental disease: first, inherited aspects of
character; secondly, adverse events in life experience (or lack of positive
experiences); thirdly, disordered brain function; and fourthly,
maladaptive responses to mental disease.

Everyone can easily grasp that they are more or less sensitive, or more or
less anxious, than the next person and that there is a spectrum, a natural
distribution, of multiple character traits from heredity. Each character
trait usually has some advantages and some disadvantages – so for
example the very sensitive person is easily hurt but on the other hand is
more sensitive to the needs of others. Character traits determine how
vulnerable we are to develop mental illness in certain situations. When
I said this to Martha she understood the idea but didn't think she was
particularly vulnerable or at any extremes of character.

On the second point Martha didn't feel she'd had any major adverse
events in her life and had received love and care as she grew up. On
the fourth point I checked she was not anorexic or alcoholic and didn't
misuse drugs; also that she had no obsessive behaviours or inappropriate
responses to her depression such as social withdrawal. There had been
thoughts of but no actual self-harm. We were left with the third factor,
a disorder of brain chemistry, as the likely culprit.

But you'll notice that this list omits something, something enormous, in
fact elephantine – the patient's worldview. A settled view as to what her
life was all about. So when I had worked through the list of factors on
the fingers of my left hand I added the fifth, the thumb, worldview.

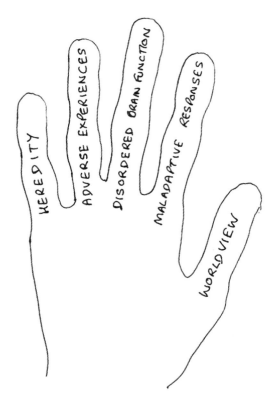

Could I give her an example, I asked? 'Yes, sure.' 'Suppose a patient has faith in Jesus Christ and is confident that ultimately everything works together for good – can you see how that worldview would affect mental illness? Or if someone hasn't thought about what life is for, or believes they live in a random universe, can you see how that would also affect it?'

Martha nodded and looked thoughtful. There was a pause. 'Actually my Dad died suddenly when I was eleven.' A great sorrow hit me. My own Dad hadn't died until I was fifty and as he had got older he had become more affectionate. Those hugs! I still miss them. And Martha had missed out on more than she even knew. In these situations, what can one say? I managed an 'Oh, I'm so sorry'. But it feels strange saying that when the death occurred 15 years previously. In these situations when I really have no idea what to say, I have found the most useful thing is to admit it and say: 'I don't know what to say'. At least that way the patient (or friend) knows you have heard, really heard, what they said.

Notice how she had already told me she'd had no adverse life events! Then as she reflected she thought of her bereavement. She did this thinking while I was giving the example of the impact of a worldview, which she was only partially listening to. This is often the way with consultations: you ask a question about one matter and then later after rumination the answer comes out. Sometimes the patient will come back after weeks to answer a question you had forgotten about – especially if they don't know why you asked it in the first place (always explain those odd questions – like asking about urinary incontinence in acute back pain!) On this occasion Martha was answering the adverse events question but also strangely enough the God question too, both at the same time. So I went on to enquire how she thought the death of her father might have affected her, and then to explore the emotional distance she always kept from others.

A GP's story

A lady with bipolar disorder was becoming increasingly manic. She was overactive and over talkative and was spending the nights awake working hard on a project to help children in an overseas orphanage. She was a Christian but felt very guilty about some of her past practices in spiritualism. She was convinced she was possessed by an evil spirit and her church had attempted to exorcise the spirit with prayer on several occasions. She attended with her exhausted husband and I immediately became aware of his hostility to her involvement with that particular church. He rolled his eyes and looked disapproving as she told her story.

When I told the patient that I was also a Christian she was delighted but the husband looked horrified. Using a text from the book of Acts, I explained to the patient that as a forgiven Christian the Holy Spirit had already entered her life and so possession was impossible. She accepted this as an authoritative comment. Then I asked her whether even Jesus took time to sleep – which she conceded he did. Then I suggested that she had been placed in a family for a purpose and that was that care for her family should be her major priority.

> *The consequence of this discussion was that the patient saw me as an ally she could trust, and this helped her to accept the therapeutic options which followed.*

Another way I try to help people visualise depression is to scribble a series of concentric circles explaining the impact of depression:

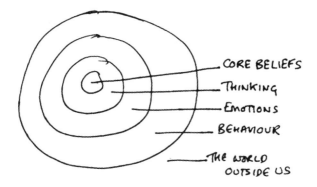

The innermost circle is core beliefs (or worldview), the next is the conscious thought life, the next the emotions and the next behaviour. Outside the 'onion' diagram is the world and we can then explore how depression is affecting and being affected by worldview, thoughts, feelings, behaviour and perception of the outside world and how different treatments can tackle different levels of the onion. So, for example, continuing to do sport (behaviour) is one way towards restoration of mental health. Or continuing to watch the news several times a day is unhelpful in depression.

We are so familiar with psychotherapy and antidepressants that it is relatively easy to forget the impact of worldview on both the causes and treatment of depression. There are numerous ways to treat depression at the different levels.

Generally because of poor concentration levels depressed patients don't read a lot. [136] Psalms are usefully brief, and many are cries from distress which depressed patients easily echo while at the same time nurturing their faith.

A GP's STORY

A lady with depression came to see me. She felt guilty for feeling depressed because she felt that as a Christian she should not feel depressed. I showed her a Psalm in which the depressed psalm writer cries out to God from the depths: with that authority she accepted that there was no need for false guilt. She then accepted some tablets for the depression.

A GP's STORY

Jake had been a patient for many years before he revealed the extent of his inner pain. The telltale signs had been there in his unwillingness to shake hands, his persistent insomnia, and his painful difficulty in making friends socially. It took perhaps 15 years before he could finally tell me his story. It came out in little bits and pieces. As we put the jigsaw together he began to understand the truth about himself. Jake's father was alcoholic and his mother was obsessionally tidy.

For no reason that he could determine, in the middle of the night he would hear his dad's heavy footfall on the stairs before the bedding was pulled back and he was thrashed. It was completely unpredictable. From as early as he could remember this happened, and he would lie awake in fear dreading the moment. He could never please his dad, no matter how hard he tried, and his mother felt powerless and did little to defend him. Eventually in a fit of fury as an older teenager Jake struck his dad and threw him out of the family home.

Jake tried to work, but he kept having to clean his computer keyboard if anyone touched it or to wash his hands. He couldn't bear the thought of other people's bugs on his magazines or in his flat, and gradually his friends deserted him when they were ordered not to touch this or that. He found sleep impossible and yet was always tired.

The thing that really surprised me was that he was consumed with guilt. His life was a failure as far as he was concerned and because of his obsessive tendencies any thought of an intimate relationship

*with a partner in the future was out of the question. He gradually
came to see that false guilt had been put on him by his parents.
When I tentatively opened up the 'God' question he said he believed
in God, so I offered to pray with him and he accepted at once.
I prayed for an awareness of God's love and acceptance of him, and
of the free forgiveness and the chance for a fresh start in Christ.*

*He was immensely grateful and for the first time since I had known
him gave me a wonderful smile. He was a great reader so I lent him
a series of books which he devoured, re-read and lent to friends.
One of his friends was transformed as a result of reading one of
these books, which was in turn an encouragement to my patient.
He still needs the miracle of overcoming the fears that his obsessions
bring and he has yet to discover the true freedom that should be his.
At last he is engaging with psychotherapy. One day I hope he will
offer to shake hands with me, and know the blessing of peaceful
sleep and intimacy with another.*

When memories have become tyrants, I have many times endeavoured
to pour self-worth and encouragement into these situations, so I was
interested in a different approach described by a pastor. Mark Buchanan
describes how his attempts at banishing the dredged up horror stories
from a counsellee's past always seemed to go wrong, and then one day
he felt 're-oriented' by God. He discovered the secret of encouraging
people to nurture great expectations of a transformed future with
Christian faith – 'what will happen matters more than what has
happened'. [137]

When it comes to psychotic illnesses psychiatrists are often
understandably cautious about exploring worldview, as religious themes
in delusions are quite common. One psychiatrist on a ward round met
a patient who introduced himself as Napoleon. The doctor asked him
how he knew he was Napoleon? 'God told me' said the patient, at
which point there was an angry voice from a neighbour, 'No, I did not!'

Patients have occasionally asked me if I thought they were possessed by
an evil spirit. After enquiring why they ask, my reply is simple – that
I don't know. I go on to explain that as a Christian I believe that evil

spirits exist but that the kingdom of heaven is right here too. If it hasn't been done we can pray through Christ that any evil spirit will leave and for the Holy Spirit to enter. I then go on to describe what wonderful gifts we have been given in our scientific knowledge and medications and that, used rightly, we should employ them too.

A GP'S STORY

I had a patient with schizophrenia, whom I had known for some time. On one occasion on return from a holiday he came to see me and described a vision of Jesus and asked me if I thought it was a true vision or an hallucination. We discussed the content of the vision in the context of the patient and his other illnesses, and drew on what we knew of Bible teaching, and concluded that on this occasion the chemistry of his mind had been upset. He was happy to accept this.

A GP'S STORY

An alcoholic homeless lady registered with the practice. From the moment she entered the consulting room she talked non-stop at high speed looking this way and that, but never at me, as she spoke. It all suggested to me a mixed intoxication with alcohol and other street drugs. Trying to make any sense of the situation was extremely difficult, especially as her partner, from whom she was inseparable, talked fairly continuously in an intoxicated manner as well.

I thought we would get nowhere and eventually a small dose of a major tranquilliser was prescribed. Pronouncing me 'lovely' before lurching forward and planting a very alcoholic kiss on my lips, she departed, still talking. Over the next few weeks she returned quite regularly, started consistent medication and slowly the illicit drugs and alcohol reduced. Her appearance (and odour) improved, and the speech began to moderate.

The old records came and eventually she was sober enough for us to look at the previous diagnosis, 'histrionic personality disorder'. [138] *'Actually,' she said, 'I wonder if it's mainly down to the alcohol'. The alcohol, it emerged, had been an attempt to block out certain painful memories but caused her to behave in a rather bizarre fashion. She herself was immensely encouraged by her own progress, no longer dependent on the alcoholic man who had accompanied her previously and who had had to prop her upright at times.*

The change in her was helped along by consistent support in safe accommodation and regular sessions with the substance misuse service. There was communication and encouragement between the teams. When I saw her most recently, during a lull in the conversation she said, 'You're a Christian, aren't you?' I said I was and she continued, 'The thing that convinces me about Jesus is the story of the woman caught in adultery and how he let her off. He could easily have been beaten up. He was very brave to stand up for her against all those men.' There was clearly an immense resonance of the story in her own life. 'Yes,' I said, 'He really understood what men are like. And isn't his forgiveness great?' She smiled and, unusually for her, briefly made eye contact.

Religious celebrations or anniversaries can present an opportunity for fresh insights into your patient's lives, but can be a difficult time for people with mental health problems, and being aware of this is often helpful for patients.

A GP'S STORY

A man with depression, who I knew believed in God, visited me shortly before Christmas. I asked him how it would be for him. 'I hate it; it's always a miserable time for me.' 'What do you think is the point of Christmas?' I asked.

'It's a family time, isn't it? I go and sit in the corner and they ask what's wrong with me.' 'Can I try you with a different idea?' I asked. 'Go ahead.' 'Just supposing God Almighty decided to show how much he loved us and chose to identify with our suffering by coming as a baby – wouldn't that be worth celebrating?'

'It's blasphemy then, isn't it?' he replied. 'What do you mean?' I was confused. 'If God did that – it's blasphemy that I hate my life.' There was a pause, while the implications of this statement sank in for both of us.

16. PRESCRIBING TRUTH

A GP'S STORY

*An African lady attended for the results of an abdominal scan.
She had been suffering from intermittent abdominal pain brought
on by eating and had lost weight over a year. She had seen a number
of physicians, been investigated thoroughly, and tried assorted
medications without benefit. Her mood was flat; she was frustrated
that because of her abdominal pain and general tiredness she was
unable to sustain work as a part time cleaner.*

*'Do you have any family in the city?' I asked. She looked uncomfortable
and gloomy. Rather reluctantly she slowly revealed aspects of her life. She
lived alone. She had no relative in the city. Even when she was working
she couldn't afford to send money back to her brother and sister in her
home country. Her mother had died some years previously. Her father
had come to this country the previous year very ill and had died. Her
husband was in the army of her own country and she had heard rumours
he was in another country but hadn't heard from him for two years.*

*Gently I explained that one possibility was that her abdominal pain
might be linked in some way to her grief and the awful situation of
not even knowing if the man she loved was still alive – whether she
was even still married, or a widow.*

Then I said: 'May I ask if you have a religious faith that helps you?'
'I'm orthodox, like my parents,' she said, with a hint of defiant pride.
'And have you been very angry with God?' For the first time in the
consultation she relaxed and laughed with relief. 'I'm always asking
him why has this all happened to me; I'm always angry with him.'

There was a silence. 'Often we don't understand why things
happen,' I said, 'and it is quite OK to be angry'. She looked
surprised and laughed again. 'Do you by any chance have a Bible?'
I asked. 'Yes, but I haven't opened it for six months.'

'Are you familiar with the Psalms?' She looked puzzled so I got
down my Bible and turned to the Psalms. 'Oh, you mean the Songs
of David – yes.' 'Often the writer of the Songs of David is angry or
confused; you might find them helpful. So here is something else
apart from the medicine for the appetite and the constipation. Read
these two...' and I wrote down the numbers of a couple of Psalms,
'and come and see me in two weeks'.

As Christians we can 'prescribe truth' in a whole range of ways, through
what we say, through referral to spiritual counsellors or ministers,
through books lent or given, or through invitations to courses, meetings
and talks. Often there is the opportunity to follow on a discussion of
faith issues with something else. Indeed the patient will sometimes
request additional direction or help. Rarely in general practice in the UK
is there easy access to a chaplain or to Christian counselling, but where
these are present referral can be very helpful.

A GP'S STORY

Martha was a Christian lady in her 70s. She was happily married to
Jim who was the life and soul of any party. He loved her dearly and
whenever I saw them he would be making her laugh with his cheeky
sense of humour. Sadly, Jim developed cancer of the stomach and
after courageous perseverance in illness when his sense of humour
was completely undimmed, he died. Martha was inconsolable.
On one occasion when I was seeing her to review her antidepressants
more than a year after Jim's death, we were discussing the reasons
why a loving God might do such a thing.

Maybe, I tried to suggest gently, it was because she worshipped Jim so much that she had put him in the place of Jesus and had now been given some time to work out her relationship with God. She completely rejected what I said. If there was any truth in the idea, it wasn't the moment she could accept it. She was still angry with God. I was relieved that this event didn't damage our long term relationship.

God remembers we 'are dust' and perhaps can only bear so much truth at a time, so it behoves us to be gentle in our prescription of truth, even when we are fairly sure we have got the picture right. Patients have a right to tear up their prescriptions! The key to a good prescription is, of course, the right diagnosis and the patient's concordance. So consider carefully whether a prescription of truth is appropriate and, if so, just what.

Christians can use biblical quotations which seem useful to the patient. I have recommended particular Psalms, because so many of them are from the depths of the Psalmist's heart and particular Psalms fit particular moods. If a patient wants to learn about Jesus, there is really no substitute for reading one of the gospels – Luke's Gospel is a natural place to start, as he was a physician.

A GP'S STORY

A 63 year old retired nurse came to see me with sleeping problems and low mood. It turned out that her son, a married man with two young children, was dying of cancer. My patient wanted to support the family but had a bad relationship with her son's wife. There was a history of unpleasantness between them: my patient had criticised her daughter-in-law previously for her behaviour, and had felt used and unappreciated when caring for the grandchildren previously. She spoke at some length about what had happened and I listened.

Then I said, 'You need to draw on your wisdom to know what to do in this hard situation. You have a lot of life experience – I guess far more than your daughter-in-law. It reminds me of St Paul writing to the Philippians when he said 'And this is my prayer: that your love may abound more and more in knowledge and depth of insight, so that you may be able to discern what is best...' [139] *Somehow using the wealth of your experience to know just how best to love your son and his family in this situation.'*

She mentioned a sect she was a member of, and added, 'I am religious and I coped OK with my own serious illness, but I can't cope with my son's cancer'. There was a long silence. 'I can't imagine what it must feel like to see your son's suffering and feel so powerless,' I said.

She declined medication and, after arranging a follow up consultation, she left. At the end of the clinic, I asked the medical student who had been with us what he thought of this episode. He made several interesting observations. Firstly, he thought that the patient really came just to spill everything out in a safe place: to be listened to and be heard. Secondly, he didn't think the patient was in a position to take advice, but because I had complimented her experience she had been able to take in the quotation from St Paul.

The quotation had revealed the patient's religious faith and the heart of her agony, and I asked the medical student to consider what alternative question might have revealed this aspect of the patient's attitude to life. After some thought the medical student suggested: 'What is there in your life which gives you encouragement at a difficult time like this?'

A GP's STORY

After greeting John, a 70 year old retired steel worker, I first checked whether he'd seen the skin specialist about his probable skin cancer. 'Yes' he said, 'and they've given me a date to have the operation as a day case in that old workhouse place...'

'You mean the General Hospital?' 'Yes.' Then we proceeded to discuss what it was he'd come about that morning. At the end of the consultation I said I hoped all would go well with his operation. To my surprise he announced that he'd decided he wasn't going for it and wanted to cancel. Grasping the only clue to hand, I asked, 'Have your family been in this city for several generations, John?'

'Yes, as far back as we know.' 'And were any of them ever in the workhouse?' 'Yes, and when I was visiting a friend who was on a ward there and was walking down one of the long corridors, I suddenly felt surrounded by all these ghosts. It really scared me. I'm not going there again.'

'Tell me John, do you believe in God?' 'Yes.' 'Well so do I, and Jesus told us that God's love casts out fear, and this operation is really important so how about I see if we can get someone to pray with you just before the operation; would that be OK?' 'That would be fine.' Immediately I phoned the hospital and got put straight through to the chaplain's office, was able to give the details, and get the whole thing set up before the patient had even left the room.

If you are referring to a minister, don't dump your problem patients! Ensure that the minister or counsellor is equipped and supported to cope with your patient's needs. Perhaps because being referred to some unknown pastor is rather intimidating, in family medicine I have found that patients prefer to accept reading material which might help them. Books may be directed to a particular area of illness; for example Jo Swinney's book *Through the Dark Woods*[140] on dealing with depression; or books which help towards developing a skill set, such as *The Marriage Book*[141] and *The Sixty Minute Marriage*[142] for people wishing to improve their marriage, or *The Sixty Minute Father*[143] on being a great dad.

Other people's life stories can have great resonance if well matched to a patient's situation. They not only give the patient hopeful examples but can reduce the sense of isolation. Of course there are many topical books and leaflets on a huge range of subjects by non-Christian authors that I lend as well. As in other areas of life, all books present some form of worldview, because an author always reveals something of his or her worldview by the choice of material and the values presented. When I lend or give books of any kind to patients, I always warn them that the book is written from a particular viewpoint and they can ignore bits they find unhelpful. I document this warning in their case notes in their presence. Generally I would not be happy to lend a book to a patient that I had not read myself.

A GP's STORY

A Muslim lady, newly married, came for a repeat of the oral contraceptive pill. I took the opportunity to congratulate her on her recent marriage, and said that I'd been married 41 years and that my wife was my best friend. I said I hoped that she and her husband would become very best friends as the years went by. I asked if she had heard of the five languages of love, [144] *and said how we had found it helpful in our marriage. I explained the concept briefly.*

It is rare that I lend a book that is evangelistic. [145] This is because it is easy to take advantage of the power imbalance in a consultation; so generally it would only be at a patient's request, and then with the provisos as above. If a patient wishes to take things further, I feel that follow up is best done by a local church group, as I don't want to cause confusion for the patient as to my role as their professional medical advocate.

Sometimes you can lend a book which has a personal link to you, which the patient would like to read because of their interest in you as their physician – for example, one GP I know has written a gripping novel which integrates some faith issues. [146] My own mother wrote a booklet for her grandchildren explaining why she believed – and after she died and patients expressed their sympathy, a number were keen to read it, which then with several opened up exploration of their own beliefs. [147]

We have already heard of some activities that Christian doctors have made known to patients. But the possibilities are many. I have known of patients invited to marriage courses, debates on ethical issues, church gatherings in and out of hospital, language classes, church rambling groups, carol services, and corporate acts of worship for the bereaved. Christians, and perhaps Christian healthcare workers especially, should be at the forefront of spotting unmet needs and seeing how these can be met.

Sometimes when it comes to prescribing truth, there comes the opportunity to respond to the blatant:

A DOCTOR'S STORY

In frustration, a patient fumed 'God knows what's wrong!' I replied: 'Well, actually – yes'.

17. DISCUSSING FAITH NEAR THE END OF LIFE

THE GP'S STORY

I looked after a man in his mid-70s during the last three weeks of his life. He was dying of renal cancer. We hadn't met before but I really liked sitting and talking to him. One reason why I enjoyed it so much was that we had both been brought up in rural Suffolk, and so had a shared background to reminisce about. He was comfortable with pain relief from a syringe driver and his own daughter was around the house caring for him.

He told me that as a boy he'd attended Sunday School until it all stopped suddenly. He was ten years old at the time, and had a much loved younger sister who was six. One day he'd been riding up the field with his dad on the tractor. His sister had been playing at the other end of the field around an old farm implement and suddenly he saw that it had fallen over. He told his dad to be quick as he was worried his sister might be injured. His dad immediately replied, 'No, she's dead'. And indeed when they drew up to the place where she was, she was dead. From that day on his dad stopped attending church and stopped sending his son, my patient, to Sunday School. The patient had never been back to church all his life.

At the time he told me this story my own daughter was the age his sister had been when she died so I could begin to imagine something of how they must have felt. I asked him, 'So what do you believe now?' 'I believe in God, but everything froze at that moment.' 'And what about your sister, did she believe?' 'Oh yes, she was a believer at Sunday School.'

As he got nearer the end I was able to pray with him a bit. He used to enjoy that. I made the effort to make extra visits. He was not distressed. On my last visit I said to him, 'You're going to be in heaven with your sister'. And he agreed. And I think he is.

I think it's vital to challenge people to put their affairs in order in the broadest sense – their relationships, their finances, and their relationship with God. The Holy Spirit gives you that moment when their human resources run out, and they open to realities that they may have been blocking all their lives. If given the opportunity, I pray for healing and that God would make himself known. In my prayer I say that if healing is not given I ask for relief of the various symptoms. We Christians can be very prescriptive: but I think a simple faith is enough.

There is an immense amount of good literature on the care of the dying, and I want to restrict myself to the issues of professionals and faith. [148] The importance of good clinical expertise and team work cannot be underestimated at this critical time for patients and their families. Spiritual care should be a natural part of this. Daniel Sulmasy [149] highlights the particular spiritual needs in end of life care as usually centring on meaning, value, and relationships with others and with God.

Just as all carers need to have some knowledge of syringe drivers and pain relief but some are experts, so with spiritual issues it is very helpful if all are comfortable with some 'faith talk' and happy to call in a minister if that is wanted.

How does a professional carer with belief in God handle the intense longing for someone she is caring for to find God? It is a great privilege to be allowed into someone's life at this intimate time. We should be grateful that it is not us who are the judges of men's souls or the arbiters of their fate. We should refrain from judgment. Not that this absolves us from taking action. We need to be available: especially, available to listen very carefully.

Spiritual history should be incorporated with the rest of the psychological and social history in a palliative care assessment. One way of asking in this area is to say, 'People often feel very fearful at a time like this. Generally there are two things: they are scared of being dead and scared of the process of dying. Do feel free to talk about these things if you want to.'

A HOSPICE CHAPLAIN'S STORY

Often a patient says to me, 'I wonder what's going to happen next?' I reply, 'What did you have in mind, the time tea will arrive, or what happens when we die?' Their response can go either way at that moment. And if not spoken of at that time, they know they can come back to the bigger subject later if they want to.

With great restraint and gentleness we can encourage the patient to consider a good closure for their own peace of mind, and for the sake of the relatives. It is in this context that the faith question does naturally arise if it hasn't previously. This is easy when the patient knows what is happening and is willing to speak of it, but much harder with patients who are in denial. Sometimes we just respect the right of the patient not to know, when they have given the cues that they don't wish to.

A GP'S STORY

I once cared for a convinced atheist lady who was dying, and visited her a number of times during her last illness. I was keen that she have some comfort and knew she didn't believe in God, so on one occasion at the end of the visit I said, 'Would you like me to read part of a Psalm to you?' 'Yes,' she said, 'I would like that'. After I read she said warmly, 'Thank you and goodbye'. This became a regular part of my visits. There was no other interaction about faith and neither she nor I broached the subject in other ways. I've cared for many people and I can only think of one of my patients who didn't wish to discuss faith in his last days.

One hospice chaplain says to the team he works with, 'If you trust me, use me' and they do. A last minute baptism or wedding, making things possible in a non-judgmental way, should be the pattern in good palliative care. If referring to a chaplain, it is important to know to whom you are referring so that you can allay fears – people are fearful of being judged. In fact, as they become more ill, people often feel intensely judged and feel failures, so an open accepting approach is absolutely fundamental. Chaplains are well used if they are easily accessible. Ease and informality of referral with no form filling, and quick availability, can be a real boon for hard pressed staff in other disciplines.

A GP'S STORY

As I approached the house I sent up an arrow prayer: 'Please, God, this is impossible: help me make the best use of my time'. I had literally ten minutes to do this visit, a full surgery awaiting me, and after that a son to collect from nursery. Joe, the 64 year old man I was visiting, was dying of pancreatic cancer. The diagnosis had been sudden. I had found a large mass in his abdomen and the diagnosis was rapidly confirmed. He was deteriorating fast.

'You're running late, aren't you, doctor – you don't have time. I'm not in any pain you know.' But he had lost weight and was weak. I reviewed him and explained that in this situation we wanted to tackle all aspects of his care and be really holistic. If there was any issue – physical, psychological, social, financial or spiritual – we'd try and help.

'On faith issues – do you have a faith? Is there a minister you'd like to speak to?' 'No.' 'Well that's fine, but if you do change your mind it's the sort of thing we could help with.' 'No, I've never had a faith – doctor, tell me, do you believe in heaven and hell?' 'Yes.' 'Do you know where I'll go? Am I good enough to go to heaven?'

I prayed silently: 'Oh help, Lord!' and said, 'I believe in a loving and holy God, and to be fair I'm not good enough to go to heaven myself. But I believe that Jesus came and died on my behalf so that I could. Would you like to talk about this more with someone?' 'OK.' I arrived back at surgery late, but mercifully the first patient hadn't turned up. I contacted the local hospice chaplain who visited. Three days later when I visited, Joe had deteriorated but was happy: 'Doctor, I feel so lucky. I have seen what's important in life.' Within the next week he finalised his financial affairs, and also got baptised and married, with a wedding at home. He never once grumbled about his illness. He declined fast, and his blood tests showed he didn't have long. On my last visit I said 'You're going to go to heaven now and I think this is the last time I'll see you'. He was barely able to speak – he just repeatedly rubbed his wedding ring and whispered, 'Thank you'.

Shortly afterwards I was visited by Joe's widow. 'I need you to tell me what you told him. I was there when he was baptised and something very special happened. It was as if there was someone else in the room with us all and it was so peaceful.'

It is sometimes not only the relatives who have to let the person go. As we have already noted, sometimes an oncoming death is more of a psychological problem for the professionals who may have invested greatly in attempting a cure. But for a Christian, as death is not final, it is not the ultimate personal disaster.

A HOSPITAL CHAPLAIN'S STORY

Despite the best efforts of the medical team in the intensive care unit the patient was clearly dying, but the exhausted young doctor just wouldn't give up and kept transfusing more and yet more blood. He was becoming more frantic in his patently futile efforts. Eventually I spoke to him, 'It is OK to let this patient die'.

Being in a professional caring role frequently demands wisdom as people seek your advice. For children, fantasy can be worse than the reality.

A HOSPICE CHAPLAIN'S STORY

A grandmother died and her daughter sought my advice because her own ten year old wanted to see her grandma at the undertakers. I advised her to describe to the girl what she would see and ask if she still wanted to go. If she said yes, then check with her again when getting into the car to go, and again when getting out of the car at the undertakers.

I heard later what happened. The girl had said yes at every stage, and when they entered the room she went straight up to her grandma's body, climbed up, and gave her a kiss. She wanted to kiss her 'goodnight', just as she had always done, and latterly done when they visited the hospice. On the way out she said, 'I don't want to go to the funeral'.

18. BOUNDING HURDLES

H urdles to discussing worldview can be divided into those in the clinician, those in the patient, those in colleagues and relatives, and finally those in the system. They overlap of course.

HURDLES IN THE CLINICIAN

The most important hurdle in the clinician is the belief, engendered over many years of living in a secular culture, that worldview is private and irrelevant to health and life, and is not to be mentioned. This is an aspect of worldview in itself and is imbibed from the prevailing culture in society and at medical/nursing/physiotherapy school.

I well remember a slide in a talk by Denis Burkitt about medical education. [150] The picture was of the hospital car park with the doctors' gleaming vehicles shining in the sun; it was entitled 'The Hidden Curriculum'. (Message: 'when you are a doctor you can expect a big car'.) Some hidden curriculum is prominent yet unspoken like that. But some hidden curriculum is simply hidden by being quietly omitted. There can be a hidden curriculum in our teaching institutions – the importance of worldview may never be mentioned, and not examined on, implying that it must be irrelevant.

LACK OF CONFIDENCE

Another hurdle is that clinicians uncertain of their own worldview may lack confidence in exploring the patient's views. Some will be fearful of damaging the patient's faith. Others will feel they don't have the language of spirituality to explore what the patient is talking about, or to make meaningful comment beyond the bland.

In this situation an admission of ignorance can empower the patient. For example: 'I know very little about that religion; tell me how it affects your life or how you will cope with this illness?' You won't manage it with every patient! But actually this sort of conversation doesn't take as long as it sounds. Develop a form of question about worldview that you feel comfortable with and try it out; confidence will come. Revealing any uncertainty you have may help level the status issues.

The Christian may lose confidence because they have neglected their walk with Christ. The simple disciplines of the Christian life are regular prayer, Bible study, and corporate worship. If you are a Christian, clarify in your mind a good open question about the kernel of the Christian message. Formulate your own one sentence answer. Then you will be ready, should the opportunity arise, to use the question or the answer.

Inappropriate language can be an issue. When I hear a young doctor using overly technical language or talking down to a patient I cringe, but I bet I used to do it. Religious language is highly off-putting as well, so use everyday language if you are going to speak of worldview issues with a patient. Then there is the issue of time.

A TIME FOR EVERYTHING?

For many clinicians who are convinced of its importance, the biggest hurdle to exploring worldview will be time.

A PHYSIOTHERAPIST'S STORY
I work citywide with patients who have a long term need for physiotherapy. Previously I quite often had brief chats about faith with patients or their carers as things arose naturally in general conversation. It tended to happen at those doorstep moments as I arrived or left a

*house. It could be ongoing over many weeks, but I found it less likely
to happen where people had lower educational achievements.*

A lady came to a 'Christian Viewpoint for Women' [151] *meeting as a
result of our friendship, which she found helpful, though I don't
have contact now. I feel I'm one link in the chain of God's work.*

*But recently I haven't had conversations about faith. Our team has
been reduced in cost-saving cuts and one is off on sick leave. There
is a tremendous amount of work to do, and honestly I feel my main
Christian witness is to turn up and do the job.*

If you have had the time and energy to get this far in this book then
think of someone who doesn't have the luxury of those gifts. In the
tough situation above there is a commitment to patients which shines
through. I worry that if there is no time for normal human contact
or for short breaks for refreshment in healthcare, then the service
will decline as staff become demoralised. Expertise will be wasted.
Our connectedness to each other in the community is one part of the
therapy, and one that is hard to measure.

When the pressure of busyness is felt we get very cautious about expressing
an interest in a patient's concerns. If you are perceived as a sympathetic ear
then opening a discussion on the meaning of life can be a recipe for trouble!
The startling thing when one studies the life of Jesus is the rhythm of his
life. He could be surrounded by demanding crowds and yet keep his focus
and meet an individual's needs with tremendous economy, and at other
times he would go into great length teaching his friends.

As with anything that is taking much too long in a clinic, there are
strategies that can be learned to postpone secondary issues: to refer, to
delegate, to set aside some future time. I know some clinicians have even
set up courses for patients enquiring about faith matters at a separate venue
so that, in their own unpaid time, things can be processed more slowly.
Personally my feeling is that medical confidentiality could be tricky in this
outside situation and generally I would refer the patient to a group that
I trusted, with suitable warnings and safeguards, just as I would process
any other referral once I had ascertained the nature of the needs.

On the time issue my experience has been that generally if the patient needed more time with me, it somehow became available, perhaps because of a cancellation by another patient. Despite this, my own consultations are often too long and patients and colleagues are (usually!) very forgiving when I do overrun. If this happens it is imperative that patients and colleagues trust you that you are not wasting time, and that when it comes to their turn, you will take adequate time and they will also be well heard and well treated.

Of course we also review our clinic and appointment time lengths regularly to try to optimise the use of the facilities and our time. It is helpful if these things are in your control, but often they are not, and if there are management pressures to hit pointless targets these can easily subvert good clinical practice. Even a brief question about faith can be very revealing, and significantly deepen the felt empathy in a consultation.

THE PAIN OF BEING INVOLVED

Then there is the hurdle of the sheer emotional pain of being involved with the suffering of others:

A SURGEON'S STORY

The little girl died in the Emergency Room. She had been in a road accident and had suffered severe intra-abdominal injuries. We couldn't save her. She was a beautiful child and the same age as my daughter and I wept that night.

It is possible to distance oneself from the patient's difficulties in self-defence so as not to be hurt or reminded of past hurts. It is also possible to be so emotionally affected as to be useless. Professionalism calls for empathy balanced with objectivity. It is not only clinicians who face exposure to highly unnatural numbers of suffering individuals. Courtesy of modern media and rolling (bad) news it is everyone's diet. It is wearying. What is a Christian perspective on this?

A GP'S STORY

Over a few months I realised I was feeling rather low and couldn't shake it off. 'Could it be grief?' I thought. I checked with the computer

– about 120 patients of our practice had died in the previous twelve months. The computer generated a list of names and I checked down it. I had known 24 of these patients extremely well over a number of years. That's two deaths a month on average. It so happens my church has an annual service for those who have been bereaved in the last year so I went along. When it came to my turn I took a flower to the communion table and laid it there with the list of 24 names. My silent prayer: 'Over to you, Lord. Thank you for these dear people and that you know grief from the inside. I miss them. I can't carry this burden. Please take it. I don't know the whole story and the future, but you do.'

In the following weeks the low mood slowly lifted.

It is tempting to insulate oneself from the emotional pain of patients and this would militate against exploration of faith. It is important to realise that it is God's job to carry the grief of the world, which he knows in total. But then he knows what's coming. Pay attention to your own need for adequate rest. The Sabbath rest is for you. If necessary, reduce your hours of work to a level which is manageable. Burnout helps no one.

HURDLES IN THE PATIENT

What about hurdles in the patient? Bob Snyder says that barriers to the acceptance of truth tend to be emotional, intellectual, volitional and social. [152] As we have said, illness often forces people to re-evaluate their worldview.

One clinician said to me that he introduces this process to people with a sentence like, 'In the context of life we have to start seeing things as they truly are'. I think many of my patients would reply to this phrasing with 'What?!' but there is a good concept there. What are the difficulties your patient is facing with regard to their worldview? We are to try to clarify and then address the problem, but only with gentleness, respect and permission – and then only when the patient is ready (this is true for each aspect of the clinical diagnosis, not just worldview of course). To ask the question another way round: God is here; what is he doing, how can I fit in with that?
In healthcare we can tackle the emotional issues of denial, antagonism, indifference and fear by our presence with the patient. Barriers to

understanding Jesus have sometimes been raised because people have been on the receiving end of the bad behaviour of Christians; if so, we need to hold up our hands and ask forgiveness for the church of which we are part. It is a demonstration of the depravity of human nature that people have used the name of God to justify or hide evildoing. God has been the biggest excuse for some of the worst deeds in human history. That is not a comment on God, but on us.

The converse reality is that Jesus Christ initiated a revolution of self-sacrificial love called the Kingdom of God which has grown ever since. As Christians, this is the project we have joined.

A good relationship builds trust and an openness to look at intellectual hurdles. The intellectual hurdles to truth which we face in ourselves and others include ignorance, misconception and error. As in any clinical situation this is done first by learning ourselves; then by education, explanation and presentation with two way communication. The process of teaching changes a teacher's understanding – as anyone who has tried to teach someone to use an insulin pen knows!

Snyder's next barrier is 'volitional' – the will. Once a clinical diagnosis is made the patient has to decide whether to run with the recommended treatment or not. In faith issues, it is understanding that Jesus is the key to God which evokes the leap of 'Yes' in our hearts to invite him in, or the 'No' to shut him out. This can be a sudden or incremental process in either direction.

To have the power to grasp change and put our will in line with God's requires strength from outside ourselves. If we haven't done it yet, this is the point at which we pray for ourselves (or in this context, our patient) for the power of the Holy Spirit.

HURDLES IN THE SYSTEM

Hurdles in the system to exploring worldview issues include tyrannical health systems management, and institutional or national restrictions of free speech. We all have a role in combating these, or upholding freedoms we already enjoy.

19. HANDLING GRATITUDE AND COMPLAINT

A GP'S STORY

Recently, after years of anxiety and depression for which he'd refused treatment, a middle aged man's life was transformed by two events. First, his manipulative dementing mother was admitted to residential accommodation and secondly he started fluoxetine.

He returned with tears of gratitude for life rediscovered. We celebrated together. My response to his outpouring of gladness and gratitude was, 'It is wonderful! I am so pleased for you. But don't thank me, you know – thank him up there'. I pointed to the ceiling and he seemed to understand that I was not referring to the practice manager in his office.

As health workers we are blessed with education and experience which give us some knowledge. Then we are granted supportive helpers, accommodation, and the tools of our trade to do good. We may have extraordinary resources at our disposal, the accumulated wisdom of many giants and heroes of our trade, a vast army of medications and procedures and specialists and therapists. We can interpret for patients the swathes of information they are trying to digest from the internet. We can clear anxious misunderstandings and gently reveal the truths about an illness. We can orchestrate signposting to support groups and

155

social supports. We meet patients when they are in distress and sometimes we are able to resolve their problem. The relief for them and the gratitude they display can be intense. It is an immense privilege. Even if we can do little and are merely present to be alongside, the appreciation may be huge.

It took some years before I started reflecting on how I responded to gratitude. I noticed that it gave me an ego boost and I started to become rather proud of my work. As a surgeon and later a family doctor I was happy for people to know of my accomplishments. Forgive me, those whom I have bored when I would have been better listening! There were more than a few times when I made errors, so it wasn't all glory, and somehow I wasn't so keen to share these.

But really, in what was good, what was to my credit? I was endowed by God with a modicum of intelligence and good health, given love and a good education by sacrificial parents, trained carefully by numerous lecturers and consultants (and patients), and had been given an adequate salary for my work. And how could I have refused the generous offer to join in Jesus' grand project, the 'Kingdom of God' and know the added gift of forgiveness? All that I have had to give had been given to me freely and generously.

Because we are in a real position in healthcare of power to help people we are in great danger. If we take credit that was due to God, then we are in the business of glory stealing. We are actually putting ourselves in the place of God. We become proud. We may even begin to believe that we are something that we are not. We may cease to acknowledge our mistakes or admit to them. We set ourselves up for a mighty fall. [153]

So how should we respond to gratitude, if it is not to inflate medical egos unhelpfully? Sometimes patients seem remarkably ungrateful for stupendous 'going the extra-mile' type of medical care. [154] On other occasions, patients are intensely grateful for a simple procedure such as clearing the ear of impacted wax. One possible response to gratitude would be to minimise the importance of what has happened. But Henri Nouwen describes the importance of taking time to accept the blessing of gratitude as a gift: [155] 'Often people say good things about us, but we brush them aside with remarks such as: "Oh don't mention it, forget about it, it's nothing…" and so on. These remarks may seem to be expressions of humility, but they are, in fact, signs that we are not truly present to receive the blessings that are given…It has become extremely difficult for us to stop, listen, pay attention and receive gracefully what is offered to us.'

Gratitude *to* us should engender a celebration of gratitude *in* us because we in turn are grateful to the ultimate giver, God, for what has been received and handed on. We can celebrate together. Church meetings are an example of one formalised way of doing this at the end of a week, but then how do we respond in the moment?

ALL CREDIT TO GOD

Jesus has actually given us very simple direction about this. He said, 'Let your light shine before men, that they may see your good deeds, and *praise your Father in heaven*' (italics mine). [156] So the question becomes, how do I respond to gratitude in such a way that God gets the credit? The old response 'Praise the Lord!' summarises well what we would like to say, but became a hackneyed phrase which sounds old fashioned and trite to modern ears – maybe it will make a comeback.

'Thank God' is another phrase that might be more usable. I have used this when writing in response to patients' letters of gratitude or gifts. I might say: 'Thank you for your gift and the encouragement which means so much to me and the staff. As far as we have been able to help you then I thank God.' Another healthcare worker I met often says to patients, 'Well it is all a gift' and indicates upward. Muslim patients, on hearing good news from me, or announcing they are better, will often say, 'Alhamdulillah' ('All praise to God') to which I might say 'Amen' and follow on with 'Thank you, Jesus'.

When they thank him, one Christian healthcare worker I met often reminds people of the story of the ten lepers whom Jesus healed. [157] In the story only one of the lepers, a despised foreigner at that, returned to thank Jesus, praising God in a loud voice and throwing himself at Jesus' feet. Jesus asked where the other nine were and commended the grateful one: 'Rise and go; your faith has made you well'. We can tell the patient that this shows that thankfulness is something that Jesus was pleased with. Jesus sets us an example of encouragement and commendation of faith when people were healed.

USING GRATITUDE TO BUILD SELF-WORTH IN OTHERS

So not only can we point to God, but we can take the opportunity which gratitude affords to encourage people with their self-worth, from a simple 'You're welcome' to a more fulsome, 'Well, you are worth a lot more than you think.' [158] Or we can congratulate them on persevering through the course of medication and treatment, which is often arduous. Or we can remind them of the courage they have shown in adversity.

We can celebrate with them the conquest of anxiety and the steadiness of faith through painful circumstances. We can share with them the fact that it has been a privilege to be able to serve in this way. We can celebrate with them the gifts of modern medicine and organised healthcare. We can return thanks to them for their encouragement of us.

COMPLAINTS AND ACCUSATIONS

Handling complaint is an uncomfortable experience at the best of times. My first reaction to complaint has been to get defensive, think of who else is to blame, become more formally polite, and on some occasions get into an argument with the patient or family member. This is a useless way of proceeding.

First, the act of facing up to the actual deficiencies in one's care of a patient involves listening to the complaint, really listening. The second secret is, of course, genuine apology. One thing that has helped me is learning to work with the complainant *what* the problem is rather than *who* the problem is, and reflecting back. One of the things which characterises a growing maturity as a Christian should be an increasing awareness of one's weaknesses, and because of a simultaneous increasing security in God's love, we should have a willingness to admit what's wrong and change. If there is no pride to defend we no longer need to be defensive! As I have said before, I have received remarkable forgiveness from some I have hurt in the course of my career.

A GP'S STORY
A 42 year old lady had been a patient at the clinic for many years. She attended our drop-in clinic and waited her turn. When she entered the consulting room she was angry that she had been made to wait so long, and asked if there wasn't a better way to organise the clinic. I apologised and we dealt with her illness.

At the end of the consultation I asked if she had any ideas of ways we could improve the service, given the unpredictability of the numbers attending. She did have some ideas and I took these to the management group. One we were able to implement; others were not practicable. I wrote to her afterwards and advised her what we were changing. Her loyalty to the clinic was actually increased and we still have a good therapeutic relationship.

Complaint is one thing but handling unjust accusation can be an extraordinarily painful business. I have known colleagues in healthcare suspended for months and years and eventually exonerated.

A TRAINEE PSYCHIATRIST'S STORY
A trainee psychiatrist was approached by a senior nurse who was aware that one of the staff psychiatrists was having a sexual relationship with an inpatient in that unit, and asked him to take some action as she was frightened for her job if she mentioned it. 'I know you are a Christian, and will know what to do,' she said.

The trainee psychiatrist didn't know what to do, as this was before good guidelines on whistle blowing and support for those who do. He faced the staff psychiatrist with the accusation and demanded that it should cease at once. The next thing that happened was that the trainee psychiatrist was himself suspended on the grounds that he was suffering delusions and a possible psychosis. He even thought to himself that was possible, as he would surely lose insight if it was true.

It was a painful time for him. Fortunately, but after some delay, he was formally assessed independently and was found healthy. The suspension itself had not been handled correctly, but the trainee

> *decided to take no legal action against his employer after he was reinstated. Meantime the scandal broke and sadly the offending psychiatrist took his own life.*

When they are unjustly accused of wrong (or psychosis) Christians are supported in this situation by the example of Christ, who was happy to retell the truth under examination, but did not use his power to defend himself, nor abuse it to hurt his accusers. The Christian should count it a privilege to suffer for doing good. Some of those mentioned in this book suffered for what they said as Christians in the healthcare setting.

All this calls for great wisdom. It is not our role to court persecution, but it is a Christian duty to support freedom of speech and conscience for all, ourselves included, if our society is not to descend back into the tyranny of gagging, which even now holds so many around the world in silent fear.

20. THE ROLE OF PRAYER

I t was 7.30am and I walked with trepidation on to City Ward at St Thomas' Hospital. In the 1970s it was the duty of us medical students to take the 'fasting bloods' before breakfast was served, as the phlebotomists (cordially known as 'the vampires') didn't start work until about 9am. City Ward was renowned for its fearsome ward sister. The bed covers were stiff, spotless white linen and were embossed with the coat of arms of the City of London. Woe betide any medical student or patient who sullied these items with anything that discoloured them, especially blood!

It was a large old 'Nightingale' Ward which had survived the Blitz. The beds were in rows down either side and the windows looked out across the River Thames to the Houses of Parliament. The patients lay stiff and straight at attention in their beds, looking more terrified (if that were possible) than me. Having collected the blood request form and the necessary equipment, I advanced towards the victim. I located the vein and just had the syringe half full of blood when suddenly, with no warning, a loud and pious voice sang out, 'Let us pray!'

At this signal the nurses, in a formation position down the ward sank to their knees with hands together. The nurse in charge read out the Lord's Prayer. I stood stock still, hoping desperately that the syringe didn't fall out of the bulging vein, or the blood clot in the needle. Fortunately no drops were spilt and the sample safely despatched.

The patients on the ward had had no choice but to listen to the prayer. I suppose at least they had some sense that the team was expressing dependency on God. Personally I suspected that the nurses had chosen their moment just to catch me out for a bit of fun.

How things have changed in 30 years! It was in December 2008 that Caroline Petrie, [159] the community nurse in Somerset, offered to pray for a patient at the end of a home visit. The patient declined. Apparently she was 'slightly taken aback' by the offer but was not upset to be asked. Another carer, on hearing about the incident, reported Mrs Petrie to the manager. The employing authority suspended her. There was a storm of public protest and she was reinstated. The *Daily Telegraph* ran a web comment forum and about 1,124 entries were made. [160] The vast majority were supportive of the nurse. Even atheists and agnostics stated that although they doubted the efficacy of prayer they would take the offer of prayer by a believer as a sign of sincere concern.

A DOCTOR'S STORY

If a problem doesn't have a spiritual root it at least has spiritual implications. I saw a man this week and toward the end of the consultation I said, 'Look, I'm not sure that medicine has that much to offer but it seems to me that I'd like to pray for you. I'd like to know where you stand on these things.' He replied, 'I don't go to church but I always pray at night.' So I prayed with him then and afterwards he said, 'Thank you, I feel so much better'.

McCord *et al's* Ohio study found that 16% of respondents to a survey wanted the doctor to pray with them. [161] But if the patient was amongst the 83% of respondents who wanted to discuss spirituality, this percentage increased to 33%. This suggests that if you discover a patient wishes to talk about spirituality, then it increases the chance that an offer of prayer would be welcomed. Most patients at least don't think prayer will do any harm.

A GP'S STORY

A young woman came to see me and described mood disturbances related to her experiences with a Satanic cult. It was a thorough discussion and exploration around the issues. She knew of my faith and appreciated that I didn't discount her experiences as fantasy. At the end of the consultation and after discussing what she would do, I said, 'Would you like me to pray for you?' She reacted with a loud and fearful, 'No!' 'Well, I'm sorry,' I said, 'But I already have'.

A GYNAECOLOGIST'S STORY

A Spanish lady was awaiting an operation. She was a colourful character, a Roman Catholic, and absolutely terrified as I took the consent. 'I'm terrified and I've been asking that God would look after me.' Thinking this would be a supportive moment I said, 'Would you like me to say a short prayer for you now?' She looked horrified, 'Not now!' 'That's fine, I'd happily pray for you later if you want me to.'

We can have extraordinary access to our creator. Jesus prayed out loud for the benefit of his followers, [162] so they could work out what was happening. But he also advocated prayer in secret, [163] and Christians can cultivate their walk with God in silent prayer at any time. Prayer for the Christian should become a natural part of life in those moments between things when we reflect on issues. It helps us keep an open ear to ideas of what he wants us to do. Sometimes when faced with suffering, prayer is the only language possible.

A NEONATOLOGIST'S STORY

The problem of working in a neonatal intensive care unit is that it is easy to be caught up in the drama of each situation and just move from drama to drama. It is very intense. But I want to live with an awareness of the spiritual context. So when I'm standing at the blood gas machine, waiting the 20 seconds it takes to process the blood specimen, I pray for the baby and the situation. There are numerous brief moments like this in the day. Having a cup of tea. Even going to the loo! Walking from the outpatient department to the office with a bundle of case notes I pray for the children they belong to. It helps me remember that God is already in the situation. Christ is in the clinic.

AN OBSTETRICIAN'S STORY
*Whenever I deliver a baby or when I'm stitching an episiotomy
I silently pray for the baby. I was particularly stimulated to do this
when observing Muslims whispering the names of God into the
baby's ear so as to be the first thing the baby hears. Amongst my
prayers I pray that the baby will come to know Jesus, and God
as Father.*

Muslims often accuse Christians of prayerlessness with good reason, but it can be an apparent prayerlessness because silent, secret prayer is unseen. Sometimes I will just allow patients' names and faces to go through my mind, naming them and praying something appropriate for them. My own Muslim patients have always been glad when I have offered to pray for them, and often they have reciprocated and promised prayer for me.

As to the content of prayers – I usually include what is on my heart for the patient: the immediate physical needs, their emotional state, their social situation or their relationship with God, according to the situation. Personally I am happy to pray for healing with the proviso 'if it is your will at this time, God'. I am not happy with prayers that imply that if only the patient had more faith then God would answer – this is a recipe for false guilt when no improvement is seen.

Prayers don't need to be long or fancy, and be careful not to use jargon. I see any improvements in health or wellbeing as the gracious gift of God, and if healing occurs without a physical explanation (rarely in my experience), I think it is because we don't understand how the laws of the spiritual world intersect with the physical. A change of heart (in the psychological, social or spiritual sense) can be just as wonderful to witness as any physical improvement.

Then there is the privilege of prayer with others. One amazing group of people are those who get together to pray for the clinic where I work. Some of our Christian patients initiated it (we obviously needed praying for!) and they pray imaginatively and regularly for us. Praying with other members of the healthcare team is another worthwhile activity which is easily squeezed from busy schedules.

Finally I want to mention the importance of regular personal devotions for the healthcare worker. As an activist, I have always found it hard to spend time in personal prayer. The following story illustrates what can happen when someone does prayerfully reflect on their work.

AN EMERGENCY ROOM DOCTOR'S STORY

In my busy department there are frequently episodes of resuscitation. When these are unsuccessful, there comes the moment when it is plain that the attempt to resuscitate the patient should stop. As the doctor in charge, my habit was to say something like, 'OK everyone, thank you very much, we shall stop now. Time of death is 14.25. Cause of death myocardial infarction.' And then we would all carry straight on with our other activities; perhaps I would go off and see someone with a broken ankle.

As I was praying about my work, I felt a conviction from God that I was treating death too lightly. One day instead of my usual resuscitation stopping statement I said something like, 'OK everyone, thank you very much, we shall stop now. Time of death 14.25. Cause of death myocardial infarction. Let's have a moment of silence; something very significant has just happened, a person has lost their life.' And I closed my eyes. After a few seconds I opened my eyes, and half the team were weeping. Later on, one by one, staff came to me and asked me 'What was all that about?'

This doctor was helping to rehumanise the team after a precise technical procedure to try to save a life. Christians and others need to work together to do this. As and when staff wanted to know how this idea had arisen, the doctor was able to point to his relationship with Christ. And as Charles Dickens has it: 'Heaven knows we need never be ashamed of our tears, for they are rain upon the blinding dust of earth, overlying our hard hearts'. [164]

21. THAT YOU MAY KNOW

'Our people – our patients – we are so privileged: They share their feelings, their sorrows and their secrets with us.' [165]

'I will give you the treasures of darkness, riches stored in secret places, so that you may know that I am the LORD.' [166]

It is one of the great privileges of being a physician or nurse to be alongside people in the confusing suffering of illness and to try to help them make some sense of it and go through it. Because of Jesus, the Christian should bring a unique perspective to the scene.

This is because the sufferings of Jesus shed a particular light on all suffering. Christians are regularly immersed in the contemplation of this in their meetings. Before his death Jesus was deserted by his friends, and betrayed to an unjust trial. His experience of the loneliness of suffering was evident in his cry from the cross as he was crucified: 'My God, my God, why have you abandoned me?' [167]

Christians believe that God vindicated Jesus' unjust suffering by raising him from the dead. Jesus then promised that no one ever again need be completely alone; he would send his Spirit to people who were willing to invite him in.

A JUNIOR DOCTOR'S STORY [168]

One of the most rewarding moments of my career to date was in Madagascar, where I was able to hold the hand of a child and pray with him as he died.

Christians are not in despair in a hopeless, chance universe of ever increasing entropy. The promises of God are of freedom to live worthwhile lives now and with a future of living forever. The expectation of a future body like Jesus' resurrected body, a transformed creation, and good relationships are part of the astounding Christian hope. 'The Christian knows something of how those words, suffering and glory, go together.' [169]

Christian clinicians try to model something of this future in the present and want to hold out this love and hope to patients. If we can be there and try to understand the patient's beliefs, and then to illuminate these treasures, we may help them discover that they are worth more than they ever imagined.

Michael Ramsey, the former Archbishop of Canterbury, said that the first characteristic of the Christian life is the humility of one who knows that he has been forgiven again and again. [170]

A JUNIOR ANAESTHETIST'S STORY [171]

The anaesthetic SHO was asked to see an old man on the ward with intolerable pain due to metastatic prostatic cancer in the spine. He inserted an epidural and started a local anaesthetic infusion, thus relieving the immediate pain, then began to talk to the old man. It was night and the ward was quiet. It became clear that the old man was heartbroken because he was estranged from his alcoholic daughter. He longed to be reconciled with her before he died, but could see no reasonable prospect for this. He also felt guilty because he had neglected his God. He felt it was no good turning to God at the end after a lifetime of ignoring him.

When asked if he would forgive his daughter if she returned he said that of course he would; the longing could be seen in his face. When asked if he thought that God too would forgive him if he turned to him, he burst into tears as this point came home to him. As it happened, his back pain did not recur although the epidural infusion was taken down. He was reconciled to his daughter who was seen pushing him round the hospital in a wheelchair.

In former times people turned to religious leaders for truth to comfort, and for wise advice. With the rise of western medicine healthcare staff have often become the new priests and confessors, with massive hospitals as great temples to health. Mostly we are trusted to keep secrets and tell the truth as we see it. So when existential questions do arise we need to be ready.

Small questions and gems of truth, shared at the right time and in the right way, build together into a transforming understanding and relationship and sometimes even healing. We can learn from that great physician, Jesus, who moved with great economy and incisive words to touch the patient's life at their point of greatest need, combining physical healing with psychological, social and spiritual restoration.

In most medical consultations a patient's underlying beliefs are not mentioned. It is usual for patients and clinicians to take each other's worldview for granted for the sake of brevity. So while I hope this book has encouraged you to engage in more such discussions, there will be very many encounters where such conversations are not appropriate.

St Paul was convinced that God determined the times and the exact places for men's lives with the specific intention that they might reach out and find him. [172] This idea, that over the course of the millennia, God has worked through creation to bring about you and me is quite astounding. When applied to the healthcare encounter it implies that this time and place, now, was actually planned in the mind of almighty God a long time ago.

To trust that idea is to expect remarkable possibilities both for the patient we serve and for ourselves, known through and through as we both are, to God. We can be confident that when we make a bad job of it we can turn to him for forgiveness and a fresh start. We can try to discern what is best at each given moment.

REFERENCES

PREFACE

1   If you want to know what 'sort' of Christian, then just read on and try
     and work it out.
2   'Two things are infinite: the universe and human stupidity; and I'm not sure about
     the universe.' (Albert Einstein, 1879-1955)
3   See Thomas Klee's discussion of Michael Balint's ideas in: Klee T. The Function
     of Balint's Levels of Mind in Balint Groups. *Journal of the Balint Society*, 2008
     drklee.com/balintarticle.htm
4   Ancient Greek: 'I have found (it)'. Running around town naked after such an
     epiphany, as Archimedes is said to have done, might not be wise.

CHAPTER 1. INTRODUCTION

5   For a discussion of competing views as to how to value human life see: Wyatt J.
     Matters of Life and Death – Human dilemmas in the light of Christian faith.
     IVP/CMF; 2nd edition 2009: 51-82, 151-156
6   Reductionism: An attempt or tendency to explain a complex set of facts, entities,
     phenomena, or structures by another, simpler set. 'For the last 400 years science
     has advanced by reductionism ... The idea is that you could understand the world,
     all of nature, by examining smaller and smaller pieces of it. When assembled,
     the small pieces would explain the whole.' John Holland.
     www.answers.com/topic/reductionism
7   The term 'disease palaces' was first used by David Morley in: Morley D.
     Paediatric Priorities in the Developing World. Butterworth, London 1973
8   For a discussion of consumerism and healthcare see: Wyatt J. *Op cit* p37-38
9   Rude medical slang, formerly used for an unintelligent patient. '*Betz cells*':
     pyramidal cells of the cerebral cortex used in cognition; '*-penia*': want or deficiency.

10   Nurse suspended for prayer offer. *BBC News*. 1 February 2009.
     news.bbc.co.uk/1/hi/england/somerset/7863699.stm
11   Charity worker suspended for Christian beliefs on homosexuality. *Times Online*.
     4 April 2009. *www.timesonline.co.uk/tol/comment/faith/article6093378.ece*
12   Wynne-Jones J. *Secularists Claim Chaplains are a Waste of Taxpayers' Money*.
     2009. *http://blogs.telegraph.co.uk/news/jonathanwynne-
     jones/9414557/Secularists_claim_chaplains_are_a_waste_of_taxpayers_money/*
13   Shock decision against Council worker sacked for mentioning God. Christian
     Legal Centre, August 2010. *www.christianlegalcentre.com/view.php?id=1156*
14   There is balm in Gilead. Traditional African-American spiritual.
15   The concept that between our evil doing and the natural consequence, death, we
     are given a space in which judgment is mercifully suspended so that we have time
     to respond to God's overture of love in his revelation of himself in nature and in
     Jesus Christ. Attributed to Valson Thampu.

CHAPTER 2. THE IMPORTANCE OF PATIENTS' WORLDVIEWS

16   Worldview: 'The overall perspective from which one sees and interprets the world;
     a collection of beliefs about life and the universe held by an individual or group'
     www.thefreedictionary.com
17   I will be using 'faith' in this sense of trusting action, rather than in the sense of
     'religion' as in the phrase 'world faiths'. The apostle James finds faith and action
     inseparable: 'Faith by itself, if it is not accompanied by action, is dead'. James 2:17
18   China and Britain clash over execution. 29 December 2009. Reuters.
     www.reuters.com/article/idUSTRE5BS08L20091229
19   Gerald Coates. Quoted with permission.
20   Jan Stafford. Quoted with permission.
21   There is a very readable summary of the attitudes of the major religions to
     suffering in: Dickson J. *If I was God, I'd End all the Pain: Struggling with Evil,
     Suffering and Faith*. Matthias Media 2003; Chapter 2
22   Genesis 15:6
23   Brand P and Yancey P. *Pain, the Gift Nobody Wants*. Diane Publishing Co 1999
24   Phrase popularised by Jane Fonda's workout videos in 1982, considered an
     'American modern mini narrative' by David Morris in: Morris DB. *Belief and
     Narrative. The Scientist* 2005;19. *www.the-scientist.com/2005/03/28/S14/1*
25   There are numerous texts that I have found useful, especially: Yancey P.
     Where is God When it Hurts? Zondervan revised 1997, and also: Lewis CS.
     The Problem of Pain. Geoffrey Bles 1940. Reissued by Harper Collins 2002
26   Revelation 21:2-4
27   McAll FAM. *For God's sake, Doctor!* Grosvenor Books 1984
28   For a brief introduction to some aspects of metanarrative see
     www.postmodernpreaching.net/metanarrative.htm
29   Acts 17:26,27
30   1 John 1:8,9
31   Hebrews 12:2
32   Monroe M *et al.* Primary Care Physician Preferences Regarding Spiritual Behavior
     in Medical Practice. *Arch Intern Med.* 2003; 163: 2751-2756

33   Holmes J. *John Bowlby and Attachment Theory (Makers of Modern Psychotherapy).* Series Title: Maker of Modern Psychotherapy. Taylor and Francis Ltd 1993

34   For a fascinating discussion on autobiographical competency see: Gwen Adshead. Capacities and dispositions: reflections on Good and Evil from a forensic psychiatrist. *www.rcpsych.ac.uk/PDF/adshead.pdf*

35   For a clear look at the psychological management of traumatised patients see: Adshead G and Ferris S. Treatment of victims of trauma. *Advances in Psychiatric Treatment* 2007; 13: 358–368

36   Some discussion of worldview and the understanding of patients with PTSD is found in: Adshead G. Psychological therapies for post-traumatic stress disorder. *British Journal of Psychiatry* 2000; 177; 144–148

37   Dickson J *Op cit*

38   Woody Allen. Quote: 'It's not that I'm afraid to die. I just don't want to be there when it happens.'

39   Death with Dignity Act. Annual report 2009. Oregon. *www.oregon.gov/DHS/ph/pas*

CHAPTER 3. THE IMPACT OF FAITH ON HEALTH OUTCOMES

40   Koening HG. Taking a Spiritual History. *Journal of the American Medical Association* 2004; 291: 2881

41   A wide ranging review is found in: Koenig HG. *Medicine, Religion and Health; Where Science and Spirituality Meet.* Templeton Foundation Press 2008

42   Roberts J *et al.* Factors influencing views of patients with gynecologic cancer about end-of-life decisions. *Am J Obstetr Gynecol* 1997;176: 166-72

43   Hummer R *et al.* Religious Involvement and US Adult Mortality. *Demography* 1999; 36 Number 2: 273-285

44   Hall D. Religious Attendance: More Cost-Effective Than Lipitor? *The Journal of the American Board of Family Medicine* 2006; 19:103-109

45   Krause NK. Religious Involvement, Gratitude, and Change in Depressive Symptoms Over Time. *Int J Psychol Relig* 2009; 19(3): 155–172

46   McCord G *et al.* Discussing Spirituality With Patients: A Rational and Ethical Approach. *Annals of Family Medicine.* 2004; 2: 356-361

47   Braam AW *et al.* Religion as a Cross-cultural Determinant of Depression in Elderly Europeans: Results from the EURODEP Collaboration. *Psychological Medicine* 2001; 31 No 5: 803-14

48   Kiri Walsh *et al.* Spiritual beliefs may affect outcome of bereavement: prospective study. *BMJ* 2002; 324: 1551

49   King M and Leavey G. Spirituality and religion in psychiatric practice: why all the fuss? *The Psychiatrist* 2010; 34:190-193

50   McCord G *et al. Art cit*

51   Koenig HG *et al.* Attendance at Religious Services, Interleukin-6, and Other Biological Indicators of Immune Function in Older Adults. *International Journal of Psychiatry in Medicine* 1997;17: 233-250. Lutgendorf SK *et al.* Religious Participation, Interleukin-6, and Mortality in Older Adults. *Health Psychology* 2004; 23 No 5: 465-475

52   Nurse sacked 'for advising patient to go to church'. *Nursing Times* 26 May 2009. *www.nursingtimes.net/whats-new-in-nursing/management/nurse-sacked-for-advising-patient-to-go-to-church/5001982.article*

53   There is a useful list and summary of research papers and books (including the highly critical) at the back of Koenig HG. *Medicine, Religion and Health, Where Science and Spirituality Meet.* Templeton Foundation Press 2008
54   Culliford L. Spirituality and clinical care. Spiritual values and skills are increasingly recognised as necessary aspects of clinical care. *BMJ* 2002; 325: 1434

CHAPTER 4. SPIRITUAL HISTORY TAKING

55   Kristeller J. 'I would if I could': how oncologists and oncology nurses address spiritual distress in cancer patients. *Psycho-Oncology.* Special issue on spirituality 1999; 8: 451-8
56   For a list of relevant publications see: *www.indstate.edu/psychology/cshrs/oasis.htm*
57   McCord G *et al. Art cit*
58   Snyder B. *www.internationalsaline.org*
59   Sulmasy DP. *The Healer's Calling, A Spirituality for Physician and Other Health Care Professionals.* Paulist Press, New Jersey 1997
60   Roman Catholic
61   George Washington Institute for Spirituality and Health. *www.gwish.org*
62   Borneman T *et al.* Evaluation of the FICA Tool for Spiritual Assessment. *Journal of Pain and Symptom Management* 2010; 40: 163-173
63   Church of England
64   Anandrajah G and Hight E. Spirituality and Medical Practice: Using the HOPE Questions as a Practical Tool for Spiritual Assessment. *Am Fam Physician* 2001; 63: 81-89 *www.aafp.org/afp/20010101/81.html*

CHAPTER 5. A FORM OF DUALISM – 'THE SACRED/SECULAR DIVIDE'

65   Alderson A. Nurse suspended for offering to pray for elderly patient's recovery. *Daily Telegraph* Health News Feed 31 January 2009. *www.telegraph.co.uk*
66   For a very readable introduction to Cartesian Dualism and its impact on Western thought, see: Hwa Yung. Christian ethical thinking in the Malaysian Context. *Seminari Theologi Malaysia* p4. *www.bgu.edu/SiteMedia/_courses/reading/TOWEthicsMalaysia98%20_2_.pdf* For a more extensive discussion, see: Hwa Yung. *Some Issues in a Systematic Theology that takes seriously the Demonic.* The Lausanne Movement, Nairobi 2000. *www.lausanne.org/all-documents/systematic-theology.html*
67   For a discussion of how dualism affects Christian teaching, see: Scott N. *Dueling with Dualism.* McKenzie Study Centre 1993 *www.mckenziestudycenter.org/philosophy/articles/dualism.html*
68   For a discussion of a Christian response to determinism and dualism, see: Wyatt J. *Op cit* p130-133
69   *www.statistics.gov.uk/pdfdir/ihs0910.pdf*
70   McAll FAM. *Op cit* p93. Attitudes and prejudices will come out in all sorts of healthcare encounters whether we intend it or not. See Wyatt J. *Op cit* p118
71   For a discussion of ideas and classifications of dualism, see: *mb-soft.com/believe/text/dualism.htm*
72   Job 38:4

73   Ecclesiastes 3:1-8
74   1 Corinthians 12:12-31

CHAPTER 6. THE CONCEPT OF 'FAITH FLAGS'
75   According to Oscar London, rule number one about practising internal medicine is
      to be Jewish because 'who else but a Jew has the innate capacity for suffering that
      can get you through a working day in a medical office'! Maybe *that's* why they
      thought we were Jewish! Anyway it was best to admit we were just *Goyim*, and
      sorry to disappoint. London O. *Kill as Few Patients as Possible and Fifty-six
      Other Essays on How to be the World's Best Doctor*. Ten Speed Press 1986
76   *www.compassionuk.org*
77   Snyder B. *Op cit*

CHAPTER 7. BUILDING TRUST
78   Nouwen HJM (1932-1996). *Reaching Out: The Three Movements of the
      Spiritual Life*. Doubleday
79   Snyder B. *Op cit*
80   Alcoholics Anonymous
81   'Where "n" is a considerable number', as that revered anatomy teacher, Frank
      Stansfield, used to say

CHAPTER 8. THE CLINICIAN'S FAITH REVEALED
82   Matthew 5:13,14
83   Snyder B. *Op cit*
84   Kevin Vaughan 2009
85   General Medical Council. *Personal beliefs and medical practice*. March 2008
      www.gmc-uk.org/static/documents/content/Personal_Beliefs.pdf
86   *Ibid*
87   See Chapter 11
88   Luke 17:15-19: One of them, when he saw he was healed, came back, praising
      God in a loud voice. He threw himself at Jesus' feet and thanked him – and he
      was a Samaritan. Jesus asked, "Were not all ten cleansed? Where are the other
      nine? Was no one found to return and give praise to God except this foreigner?"
      Then he said to him, "Rise and go; your faith has made you well."
89   Luke 10:5-12
90   Empathy: 'Direct identification with, understanding of, and vicarious experience of
      another person's situation, feelings, and motives'. The American Heritage® Stedman's
      Medical Dictionary Copyright © 2002, 2001, 1995 by Houghton Mifflin Company
91   Koenig HG. *Op cit* p19
92   Hippocrates (460-375 BC)
93   Sulmasy DP. *Op cit* p67
94   Anthropocentrism is to consider human beings the most significant entities of the
      universe, or to interpret or value the world in terms of human values and
      experiences. *www.merriam-webster.com/dictionary/anthropocentrism*
95   Gideons International places Bibles in hospitals and other places. *www.gideons.org.uk*

96   Snyder B. *Op cit*
97   See it in action at: *www.arocha.org/int-en/resources/videos/5157-DSY.html*
98   Climate Stewards. *For the Life of the World.*
      www.arocha.org/gb-en/whatwedo/1715-DSY.html

CHAPTER 9. SHORTCUTS
99   Gladwell M. *Blink, The Power of Thinking Without Thinking.* Penguin 2005
100   McAll FAM. *Op cit*
101   Daniel 5:27
102   Petersen EH. *Christ Plays in Ten Thousand Places.* The 1998 JJ Theissen
      Lectures. CMBC Publications, Winnipeg 1999

CHAPTER 10. RAISING FAITH WITH COLLEAGUES
103   1 Corinthians 13:12
104   General anaesthetic
105   Matthew 5:13,14
106   A Rocha. Christians in Conservation. (A Rocha means 'The Rock' in Portuguese.
      The first project took place on the Algarve.) *www.arocha.org/int-en/index.html*
107   Bunyan J. *The Pilgrim's Progress from this World to That Which is to Come.* 1678

CHAPTER 11. JESUS AT WORK
108   The significance of this story was highlighted for me in: Fountain DE. *God,
      Medicine and Miracles. The Spiritual Factor in Healing.* Waterbrook Press,
      Colorado Springs 1999. It is also beautifully portrayed in the film *The Miracle
      Maker,* directed by Derek Hayes. Ffilmiau S4C Films 2000
109   See Leviticus 15:19-30

CHAPTER 12. IS IT POSSIBLE TO BE LIKE JESUS?
110   Sulmasy DP. *Op cit* p51
111   John 14:1
112   John David Marsh, 1925-2004
113   Origin unknown, often attributed to St Francis of Assisi
114   Emerson RW. Quote
115   Smith GA. *The Life of Henry Drummond.* Doubleday and McClure Company
      1891. Henry Drummond was slightly misquoting Alfred, Lord Tennyson's *Ulysses*
116   Hebrews 12:2; Revelation 21:3,4
117   Sulmasy DP. *Op cit* p47
118   Revelation 3:17,18
119   Soo EJ, editor. *Beyond Datelines and Deadlines, Life affirming testimonies from
      journalists and other media related people.* The Star Christian Fellowship,
      Selangor, Malaysia 2005
120   Peterson EH. *Christ Plays in Ten Thousand Places, A Conversation in Spiritual
      Theology.* Hodder & Stoughton 2005. p18

CHAPTER 13. BUILDING SELF-WORTH AND DEALING WITH GUILT

121 Dalrymple T. *Life at the Bottom*. Ivan R Dee, Chicago 2001
122 Jones J. *Thought for the Day*. BBC Radio 4, 22 April 2009.
     Full text at: *www.liverpool.anglican.org/index.php?p=698*
123 Matthew 7:11
124 Matthew 6:19
125 For a discussion of domestic violence and some factors that promote it,
     see Chapter 4 *Tough Love* in Dalrymple T. *Op cit*
126 Augustine. *Confessions*. 397. Book 1.
     www.ourladyswarriors.org/saints/augcon1.htm
127 John 8:34
128 Emerson RW. Quote, origin uncertain
129 John 8:36
130 2 Peter 3:9
131 Dominian J. *Forgiveness and Reconciliation*. 2001.
     www.rcpsych.ac.uk/pdf/do,inion1.pdf

CHAPTER 14. DO NOT BE AFRAID

132 Watson D. *Fear No Evil, A Personal Struggle with Cancer*. Hodder Christian
     Paperbacks 1984
133 Roberts O. Sermon on Matthew 14:22-33
134 Brady N and Tate N. Hymn: *Through all the changing scenes of life*.
     Text: Psalm 34.The Lutheran Hymnal 1696

CHAPTER 15. MENTAL HEALTH AND WORLDVIEW

135 McHugh PR. *The Mind Has Mountains: Reflections on Society and Psychiatry*.
     Johns Hopkins University Press 2006
136 There are numerous books on depression. One useful and engaging resource,
     born out of personal experience, is: Swinney J. *Through the Dark Woods*.
     Monarch Books 2006. It also has a good resource list at the back.
137 Buchanan M. *The Rest of God, Restoring your Soul by Restoring Sabbath*.
     W Publishing Group of Thomas Nelson Inc, Nashville 2006. p209
138 Generally in my practice I have found the management of patients with personality
     disorders and borderline personality disorders particularly challenging. *Mad, Bad
     or Sad?* is a very helpful look from a Christian worldview at the basis and
     management of antisocial behaviours and mental disorders. The great thing about
     it is its practical optimism. Beer MD and Pocock ND, Editors. *Mad, Bad or Sad?
     A Christian approach to antisocial behaviour and mental disorder*. Christian
     Medical Fellowship 2006

CHAPTER 16. PRESCRIBING TRUTH

139 Philippians 1: 9,10
140 Swinney J. *Op cit*

141 Lee N and Lee S. *The Marriage Book.* HTB Publications 2000
142 Parsons R. *The Sixty Minute Marriage.* Hodder and Stoughton 1997
143 Parsons R. *The Sixty Minute Father.* Hodder and Stoughton 1997
144 The five love languages are: Words of Affirmation, Quality Time, Receiving Gifts, Acts of Service, and Physical Touch. See: Chapman GD. *The 5 Love Languages.* Northfield Publishing, Chicago 4th edition 2010
145 Patients have expressed appreciation for: Palmer B. *Cure for Life: A Prescription for the Meaning of Life.* Christian Medical Fellowship 2006, and: Williams P. *If You Could Ask God One Question.* Good Book Company 2007
146 Sharp AJH. *The Ghosts of Eden.* Picnic Publishing 2009
147 McAll FAM. *Beyond Belief.* John Faber 2006

CHAPTER 17. DISCUSSING FAITH NEAR THE END OF LIFE

148 One very practical and moving booklet that I have used with patients' relatives is: Casson JH. *Dying, the Greatest Adventure of my Life.* Christian Medical Fellowship 2nd edition 1999
149 Sulmasy DP. *Op cit*

CHAPTER 18. BOUNDING HURDLES

150 Denis P Burkitt, 1911-1993
151 Christian Viewpoint for Women is now known as Activate. *activateyourlife.org.uk/page/about-activate*
152 Snyder B. *Op cit*

CHAPTER 19. HANDLING GRATITUDE AND COMPLAINT

153 'Pride goes before destruction, a haughty spirit before a fall.' Proverbs 16:18
154 'If someone forces you to go one mile, go with him two miles.' Matthew 5:41
155 Nouwen H. *Life of the Beloved, Spiritual Living in a Secular World.* The Crossroad Publishing Company, New York 2001
156 Matthew 5:16
157 Luke 17:11-19
158 Matthew 6:26; Luke 12:7

CHAPTER 20. THE ROLE OF PRAYER

159 *www.telegraph.co.uk/news/newstopics/religion/4537452/Nurse-Caroline-Petrie-I-will-continue-praying-for-patients.html*
160 *www.telegraph.co.uk/health/healthnews/4446935/Nurses-prayer-suspension-Sign-petition-for-Caroline-Petrie-here.html*
161 McCord G *et al. Art cit*
162 John 11:42
163 Matthew 6:6
164 Charles Dickens (1812-1870). *Great Expectations.* Chapter 19

CHAPTER 21. THAT YOU MAY KNOW

165   Field S, Chairman of the Royal College of General Practitioners, UK. Keynote speech, RCGP national conference, Harrogate, October 2010: *'I think back to what Don Berwick said when he addressed our conference and spoke movingly about his father – a GP in the United States. I remember his description of his father's vocation, when he said "His privilege was to enter the dark and tender places of people's lives – our people". Our people – our patients – we are so privileged: They share their feelings, their sorrows and their secrets with us.'*

166   Isaiah 45:3. Note that God's name in Hebrew, YHWH, is rendered LORD in block capitals in many English translations. This follows the Jewish rendering YHWH as 'Adonai' (out of reverence for the holiness of the name) when the scriptures are read aloud.

167   Matthew 27:46. Jesus was quoting Psalm 22 which, as a good Jew, he knew by heart – a cry of anguish but not despair. I suggest reading the whole Psalm to grasp his thought.

168   Parsonsons V. To pray or not to pray? *Triple Helix* Christmas 2010:11

169   Ramsey M, former Archbishop of Canterbury. Sermon: *Christ Crucified for the World*. St Aldate's Church, Oxford 27 January 1963. Quoted in Hicks R. *The Endless Adventure*. London, Blandford Press 1964

170   Ramsey M. *Op cit*

171   Vernon G. As water is to fish, so is society to people. *BJGP* 2011; 61(582): 74-5

172   Acts 17:26

christian medical fellowship

uniting and equipping christian doctors

To find out more, telephone 020 7234 9660 or visit our website www.cmf.org.uk

CMF, 6 Marshalsea Road, London SE1 1HL
Tel: 020 7234 9660 Fax: 020 7234 9661
Email: info@cmf.org.uk Website: www.cmf.org.uk